A Management Guide to
AUTOMATED
ASSEMBLY

FIRST EDITION

published by

VIRES ACQUIRIT EUNDO

The Institution of Production Engineers
Rochester House, 66 Little Ealing Lane, London W5 4XX

CONTENTS

Introduction

Appendices

Working Party

This publication has been compiled for
The Institution of Production Engineers
by the Working Party listed below:

G. Wittenberg, CEng, FIMechE, FIProdE (Chairman of Working Party)
Rhoden Partners Ltd.

R. J. Christmas,
Ronson Products Ltd.

J. Coates, BA(Econ), MA, Phd, ACMA
The University of Aston Management Centre

D. W. Gatehouse, CEng, MIMechE,
Wolfson Industrial Automation Group,
The University of Nottingham

G. Greenhalgh, BSc(Tech), CEng, FIMechE, FIProdE, MBIM,
Cramic Engineering'Company Ltd.

P. G. L. Scott, CEng, MIMechE, MIProdE,
V & E Friedland Ltd.

R. M. Webb, CEng, FIMechE, FIProdE, FIQA,
The Institution of Production Engineers

Technical editing:
L. J. Weaver, CEng, FIProdE, MIEE, FINC,
Director, P-E Consulting Group

INTRODUCTION

THE PURPOSE OF THIS BOOK is to help managers formulate and influence company policy concerning automated assembly. To many managers this will be a new subject which may be thrust upon them quite suddenly as a result of a new product development, a market change or a shortage of labour. It is very likely that interest in automated assembly will arise in conjunction with efforts to improve productivity, reduce costs and generally improve manufacturing efficiency. However, because automated assembly is a comparatively new industrial activity, the manager may not be able to fall back on his training and experience in order to assess its relevance and merits.

One aim of this Management Guide is to enable a manager to find out quickly whether automated assembly is for him; at a given time, in his company, for a particular product range. If it is, the Guide seeks to show him how to plan and implement a project, whom to involve, the benefits and the risks. Though the subject is fairly new, or perhaps because of it, automated assembly is something of a vogue topic and some companies have rushed into it without clear aims or a chance of success. Once bitten, they may be twice as shy and thus miss a real opportunity when it occurs. Moreover, reports of unsuccessful projects can soon get a new technique into disrepute. Automated assembly is too important to be exposed to this risk, for when properly applied to suitable products it gives a manager an exciting and powerful tool for sweeping away or at least greatly improving an otherwise intractable and frustrating industrial activity—labour-intensive and monotonous manual assembly work.

There are not many techniques potentially as powerful as this one in the quest for greater productivity, more consistent product quality, greater industrial efficiency and better working conditions, provided the hazards of misapplication, false starts, wrong objectives, inadequate budgeting, unsuitable equipment and neglected industrial relations can be avoided.

The authors hope that this first edition of the Management Guide to Automated Assembly will soon be out of date, in its practical aspects if not in the underlying thoughts and arguments. Thus, they have written for the present moment, discussing today's means and methods to help the reader solve his problems now. May the successful application of their knowledge and ideas soon make a second edition inevitable.

Further information on automated assembly techniques is available in an excellent set of 20 volumes of Data Memoranda giving very detailed design information under six subject headings. The Data Memoranda, and a leaflet describing them, are obtainable from the Publications Department, The Institution of Production Engineers, Rochester House, 66 Little Ealing Lane, London W5 4XX.

CHAPTER 1

THE CASE FOR AUTOMATED ASSEMBLY

INTRODUCTION

In the past the term automated assembly has generally been used when referring to the installation of special purpose equipment which automatically performed a number of assembly operations that had previously been carried out manually. In the great majority of cases automated assembly meant that the human effort required to carry out a number of simple assembly operations was replaced by mechanical devices which were operated by pneumatic, electrical or hydraulic activators. However, although the use of devices was frequently very ingenious and resulted in some reduction of manufacturing costs, the degree of automation achieved was limited. In many instances, it enabled an assembly operator to achieve a higher and more consistent output but did not actually replace him.

Today, the term automated assembly has wider application and is more generally understood to mean the total replacement of the physical and mental functions of an operator by automatic means. More importantly, it has wider significance in the context of our present industrial climate for both economic and technological reasons. It has been estimated that more than half the people employed in manufacturing industries are engaged on assembly operations. The cost of this labour will almost certainly rise substantially in the future and the labour itself is likely to become increasingly dissatisfied with tedious and monotonous work. Recent technological developments in the fields of high precision sensing, micro-processor control and servo-mechanical devices have greatly improved the feasibility of automated assembly projects which only a few years ago would have been regarded as either totally impractical or pro-hibitively expensive. There is thus much greater need and scope for the application of partially or fully automated techniques to assembly operations.

This chapter sets out some of the typical reasons for considering automated assembly and the benefits to be derived from its successful implementation; it then goes on to acknowledge how the approach to automated assembly may be influenced by company size and concludes by reviewing very briefly the way in which such a project should be tackled.

TYPICAL REASONS FOR CONSIDERING AUTOMATED ASSEMBLY

A number of reasons usually combine to provide the justification for automated assembly but the order of preference of these reasons will inevitably vary, depending on the volume and nature of the products concerned. However, some of the more important reasons for considering automated assembly are briefly summarised below:

1. Reducing dependence on manual labour

The scope and desire for labour-saving is generally the main reason for considering the introduction of automated assembly and the prime objective is, of course, to reduce the labour cost of the product. The most favourable conditions exist when the quantity of assemblies is large, the product is expected to have a long life-span, and the existing assembly operations involve significant numbers of operators. There are, however, a number of less obvious reasons for considering automated assembly:

High Labour Turnover: In conditions where the manually performed assembly processes are tedious, monotonous and, possibly, hazardous, it is difficult to retain labour. High turnover generates the requirement for continual training programmes for newly-recruited operators and, in addition to the expense of providing this facility, it also means that the assembly lines are unlikely to be fully manned with experienced operators performing at the optimum end of the learning curve. In these circumstances it is difficult to achieve properly balanced assembly lines, and the overall productivity of the assembly shops is likely to remain well below standard performance.

In all cases where there is high labour turnover, automation of the manufacturing processes should be seriously considered as the overall benefits can be substantial.

Scarcity of labour: Apart from the problem of training labour for assembly work, the recruitment of this labour may also present increasing difficulties. There may be a genuine scarcity of labour in the district because of the demands of other local employers, or a seasonal scarcity created by the attractions of other employment during certain times of year. In either event it could be beneficial for a company to consider embarking on a progressively implemented automation programme before attempting to entice labour from further afield.

The need to increase production may be frustrated by difficulties in obtaining suitable labour sufficiently quickly. Here again, the implementation of a stage-by-stage automation programme could result in the more effective use of the existing labour force and release some of it for re-deployment on other tasks directly associated with achieving increased production.

Fluctuations in output: In almost all companies, manual labour is subject to disputes ranging from minor disruptions, caused by incompatible personalities on the same assembly line, to complete withdrawals of labour. Even where the climate of industrial relations is excellent it is very difficult to guarantee the output from the assembly shops. Operator-paced assembly lines dominated by female labour are particularly susceptible to disruption caused by absenteeism which can arise at short notice because of family responsibilities. All these difficulties together with the manning problems caused by holidays, rest periods and illness generally combine with the result that output levels are virtually unpredictable. In consequence, quoted delivery dates may not be maintained and the actual costs of assembly will fluctuate in a manner that is difficult to control.

Although the relevance of the possible reasons mentioned above will vary from company to company, the real case for introducing automated assembly will, in the final analysis, be based on the comparison of future costs. There is no doubt that the cost of employing labour will continue to increase, whereas an assembly machine, if carefully designed and maintained by competent personnel, should continue to function for many years at a predictable cost and output.

2. Need to increase output

Increased output is normally achieved by engaging additional labour for manual assembly during normal working hours or by utilising overtime or by sub-contracting work. In any event, costs are increased and there is the additional likelihood of pay structures/incentive schemes being distorted and increased supervision and inspection services becoming necessary. In these conditions thought should be given to the introduction of automation techniques which would lead to a reduction in the labour force, but at the same time increase output.

Sophisticated equipment may have been introduced already thereby speeding up the flow of components to the assembling area. As a result, however, restrictions on output can frequently be transferred from one department to another because insufficient attention has been paid to the overall manufacturing system. In these circumstances, automating the assembly process should be considered as a means of balancing the output from different departments.

A company using traditional manufacturing techniques may find that it is competing with others who are equipped with automated means of assembling their products. A company faced with this situation may be forced to decide at an early date whether it can afford to invest in automation in order to compete effectively and remain in business.

3. Product Stability

Where there is a large quantity of assemblies and comparatively low labour cost, the economic justification for automation depends largely on the stability of the product and its expected life span. In these circumstances the financial savings are likely to result from such benefits as increased production rates and reduced work in progress.

Automated assembling techniques can also be successfully employed in circumstances where there is a relatively low number of assemblies in a single batch but a large number of batches with components of similar configuration, together with a high labour cost. A typical example of this would be in the assembly of electric switches for domestic use, i.e. single or double pole switches; single, double or treble switches per unit, etc. However, stable component design is an important requirement and the tooling features on the assembly machine will need to be of flexible design to allow the machine to cater for components of differing configuration. An example of how this might be done is illustrated below:

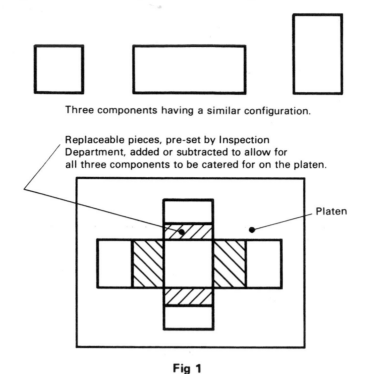

Three components having a similar configuration.

Replaceable pieces, pre-set by Inspection
Department, added or subtracted to allow for
all three components to be catered for on the platen.

Platen

Fig 1

In these circumstances, serious consideration should be given to the feasibility of grouping the components into "families" so that each "family" contains the maximum number of similar components in order to minimise the number of necessary changes to the tooling set-up.

Where there is a need to build flexible design tooling features into the machine, together with the facility for rapid-change tooling, pre-set tooling techniques can be employed. The cost of this type of assembly machine will be higher than for the conventional type, but there are many cases where these extra costs can be justified.

By incorporating, wherever practical, proven standardised features into the assembly machine, a design change to the product or even a completely different product can often be accommodated by altering the tooling areas only and leaving the basic machine base, index mechanism and the main features of the control system unchanged.

4. Product design

A very good time to consider automated assembly is at an early stage of product design. Decisions taken on component design reflect, and often establish, the parameters of the assembly machine design. At the investigation stage, it is essential that the Project Engineer responsible for automation becomes deeply involved in the component design and that his recommendations are taken into account when the component design is finalised. Close liaison between all the parties involved will certainly facilitate progress towards automated assembly and could well result in the potential development of a less costly machine than would otherwise be the case.

The investigation into the feasibility of automated assembly may well include recommendations about incorporating into the component design certain non-functional features which will assist the operation of the assembly machine. A slight change to the component configuration can allow easier orientation of the component by the feeder mechanism, faster selection of a single or group of components by the selection device, and more precise positioning of the component at the work station in the required attitude for assembling.

It is likely that the component assembly build-up suitable for automated methods of assembly will be different to that used for manual assembly methods where the component can be easily turned over and presented, sometimes at awkward angles, to the workhead. The whole approach to the assembly operation may need to be modified with certain products. For example, it may be more convenient and practical to abandon an existing method of building up a complex assembly comprising a large number of individual components in favour of grouping together a number of sub-assemblies in the way a mass-produced motor car is manufactured.

Detailed analysis of the product and the sequence of assembly operations could well reveal that it would be more sensible to build a number of simple assembly machines with each machine capable of assembling a single sub-assembly which is fed to a "mother machine" whose function is to assemble the sub-assemblies. An illustration of this arrangement is shown below:

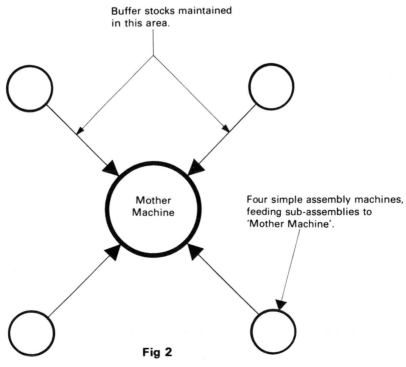

Fig 2

If the operating sequences of the machine are controlled to ensure adequate provision of buffer stocks, the amount of downtime experienced by the "mother machine" can be effectively limited. Another favourable feature of such a system is that the "mother machine" will receive for assembling only components which have already been accepted and assembled.

5. Quality Control

This area will be considered in greater detail in another section of this publication but reference is made here to quality control because the subject is so often considered to be of paramount importance when explaining the feasibility of an automated assembly system.

For the assembly machine to operate at a consistently high level of efficiency, it is essential that the components presented to the machine are maintained within the specified tolerances. Good quality control and good housekeeping throughout the complete manufacturing system are therefore important requirements for successful automated assembly. In consequence, the effective implementation of automated assembling techniques leads to better and more consistent product quality.

The need to maintain tighter quality control of components may lead to some increase in the cost of their manufacture but this cost increase is more than likely to be compensated by savings achieved in other areas. For example, the completed assemblies which are rejected at the final inspection stage because of faulty components may have to be scrapped or costly labour employed to take them apart so that other components can be salvaged.

An assembly machine can be designed to carry out an inspection function on the individual components and detect component presence. This inspection function can be performed by carefully positioned probes built into the machine control system. Should a probe fail to detect and signal the presence of a component, the machine would cease to function and so allow corrective action to be taken.

6. Other Reasons

Continued failure to meet delivery promises can highlight the time required for assembly as a major problem. Automation techniques, if properly applied, have the advantage of reducing the manufacturing cycle and the amount of work in progress.

Many companies are willing to invest in automation equipment even when there is no short-term pay-back on the investment. This decision is taken because it is recognised that it is important to build a store of "know-how" for use on future projects which, at the appropriate time, can be utilised to obtain a rapid market advantage.

It may be found that with a particular product, a high number of rejects occur during the manual assembling operation because the components are difficult to orientate, position and secure whilst the workhead is performing its assembling operation. A typical example is where minute items have to be picked up by tweezers, often under a microscope, and held precisely in position using one hand whilst the other hand operates a workhead which performs the securing operation. To deskill such an operation and release operators for other important tasks and also to provide more interesting and rewarding tasks for the operator, are clearly valid reasons for deciding to automate.

During the assembly process the product may require difficult or continuous handling which induces operator fatigue. For example, the simple operation of placing a washer over a thread stud and then running down a nut to a specified torque, can cause considerable fatigue to an operator if repeated continuously throughout the day. Fatigue of this nature can be eliminated by a well-designed automated assembling machine.

THE APPROACH TO AUTOMATED ASSEMBLY

The size of the company, whether small or large, may have an influence on its approach to automated assembly, but it is difficult to quantify the terms "small" and "large" in relation to their potential for adopting automated assembling techniques.

The factors that may perhaps be more relevant in a small company would include the following:

- it may have only one or a few products
- it may owe its success to special knowledge, or special assembling techniques that cannot easily be incorporated into automated assembling
- the decisions may be made by an entrepreneur whose knowledge may be limited or who does not have the time or opportunity to consult others, or his opportunity to obtain knowledge of automated assembling is limited
- the entrepreneur can make snap decisions, is flexible and may be enthusiastic about innovations
- the financing of a project may be difficult
- the risks may be too great for a small company to undertake if failure of the project could lead to serious financial difficulties
- the effect of breakdowns in an automated assembly system and the resulting loss of output could be more significant in a small company where the opportunity for improvisation may not exist in the short term
- it may be too dependent on a sub-contractor for the design and build of the machine
- a small company may lack the ability and facilities to maintain the sophisticated equipment properly.

The factors which might influence the approach of the large company would probably include the following:

- it has a wider choice for a potential project to automate assembly and the timing for so doing may also be more flexible

- it may have more resources and technical staff available to undertake the project and is therefore not so dependent on sub-contract designers and machine manufacturers
- the project may be delegated too far down the line of authority and not be actively progressed to fruition
- large organisations may be slow to act on implementation of the project.

Irrespective of the size of the company and related factors such as availability of technical services, market share and product range, it is important that any steps to introduce automated assembly be taken in a logical sequence. In essence, it is first necessary to obtain reliable data on volumes, mixes and labour costs which must then be viewed in the light of technical trends, competitors' activities and possible product life-spans. If there is a clear indication that the installation of some form of automated assembly equipment would have a significant impact on current and likely future assembly costs a preliminary evaluation should be made. If such a study indicated that the automated assembly project was technically feasible and would yield a good return on likely investment the machine should then be developed. The engineering and development of the machine must be carefully staged and monitored so that the economies of the project can be checked and re-checked, thereby minimising risk and potentially wasted effort.

The way in which an automated assembly project is handled will, of course, vary depending on the complexity of the assembly operation, the degree of automation sought and the past experience of the company concerned. Nevertheless, there are essential guidelines which must be observed if the project is to succeed and not founder on the many obstacles which bedevil effective progress. The following chapters of this publication set out some of these guidelines and indicate how a project should be controlled if the company is to secure the financial and other benefits that can result from the effective introduction of this exciting but, as yet, unexploited technique of automated assembly.

CHAPTER 2

AUTOMATED ASSEMBLY:
COMPONENTS AND OPERATIONS

INTRODUCTION

Automated assembly is best applied in companies making high volume products involving labour-intensive assembly operations and, in these situations, it offers significant potential benefits in terms of cost reduction and increased productivity. However, whether the full potential benefits are actually achieved does depend largely on the type of components to be assembled and the actual assembly operation. This chapter provides a basic guide to the characteristics of components and the operations which are ideally suited for automated assembly.

FEATURES OF COMPONENTS

During automated assembly a component may be tumbled, slid, rolled, dropped, stacked, pushed, lifted, queued, spun or placed. These operations can occur singularly, in sequence or simultaneously and may be aided by mechanical handling using various pneumatic, electro-mechanical, magnetic or hydraulic devices.

For these reasons the ideal components for automated assembly should:

- be consistent in shape and size
- be free from burrs or flashing
- require a minimum amount of orientation
- have enough features to allow correct orientation to be easily achieved without creating problems of interlocking
- be free from oil and swarf
- be smooth in surface finish
- be able to withstand high-speed mechanical handling without damage or marking.

The method of producing a component does have an important bearing on their suitability for automated assembly. It is therefore worthwhile reviewing in general terms some of the merits and demerits of components produced by the main manufacturing processes.

Gravity Castings (metals)

Difficult to locate accurately because of variations in finished size and surface finish, and usually necessary to provide spot-machined faces. Also important to ensure that runner and riser positions avoid machine mechanisms and locating areas and some pre-trimming may be necessary. Rough faces may cause heavy wear on mechanisms.

Pressure Die Castings
Ideal for automated assembly but flashing should be trimmed to avoid interference with work-holding stations and jamming of bulk feeders. Some mechanisms may damage the more fragile components.

Injection Mouldings (Plastics)
Ideal for automated assembly but flashing should be controlled and internal gates provided wherever possible or runners positioned to avoid interference with mechanisms and work stations. Alternatively, work stations should be designed to avoid runner-pips, otherwise hand-trimming may be needed. May be necessary to modify the moulding dies to provide lead-in on components and also to use reinforced plastics having greater rigidity, although compliance of plastic can aid assembly. Bulk feeders may damage finish.

Automatic Machined Parts
Cumulative tolerances can be a problem and must be avoided. May be necessary to monitor dimensional drift and take corrective action while machines are still cutting within limits. Components generally need to be degreased.

Pressings
Can be good for automated assembly. Large parts and difficult shapes may need magazining but burrs should be kept to a minimum or interlocking of components may occur. Important to check dimensions of batches from different press tools. Generally need to be degreased.

Fabrications
Difficulties with variability between components. May be necessary to spot-machine and to provide fixture to hold shape required. Generally difficult to avoid manual feed.

Forged Parts
Generally necessary to spot-face and to provide fixture to ensure effective positioning. Size and shape of components may necessitate hand placing.

Sintered Parts
Very good for automated assembly as dimensions are repeatable but possible difficulty in providing adequate lead on components.

COMPONENT DESIGN
When exploring the possibility of automated assembly of components it is important to question whether the assembly operation needs to be done in the same old way. What appear to be simple manual operations can become very difficult machine operations and the tendency to restrict mechanisms to carrying

out the same tasks as human operations should be avoided by good component design. To do this, it is necessary to list the tasks carried out manually to produce the assembly as well as writing down the assembly sequence. In many cases this means writing down the manual job specification thoroughly for the first time. It can then be compared with the facilities which can be offered economically on an assembly machine. The constraints imposed by the machine will entail a new job specification being written which can lead to modifications of the component parts of the assembly and, if necessary, changes in the assembly sequence.

These changes could involve modifying a component to allow mechanical identification and orientation by adding or subtracting material to create special features which are readily detected by the machine. Other features likely to facilitate assembly are a generous lead-in on holes and slots where parts are placed, combined with, if possible, good leading edges on the parts to be inserted.

In view of the foregoing it will be appreciated that the best time to consider automated assembly is during new product development or the re-design of existing products. At this stage everyone who is involved in the product from salesmen to the shop floor should be made aware of the reasons for modification of components.

If the assembly is replacing a single component to gain cost savings, for example, by producing standard ends to fit various centre sections, or to save weight by making hollow sections to replace a previous solid object, a fresh look should be taken at the product quality required together with choice of materials for the new assembly.

The salesman will need to be told if the machine is to carry out automated packing and how the customer should be educated to receive the newstyle pack. If faulty assemblies are being delivered to the customer, a knowledge of their production will help to identify the problem areas. The introduction of automation may also mean reducing the number of assembly combinations or colours which can be offered to the customer in order to keep the machine fully occupied. In fact, these observations may be the necessary prelude to the introduction of automation.

ASSEMBLY OPERATIONS

The increasing sophistication of a wide variety of handling, sensing and gauging methods combined with the facilities offered by microprocessor control provide opportunities for the automation of complex assembly operations. In the great majority of cases, however, automated assembly involves the movement and location of components which are then fastened together by a standard process. Some of these processes lend themselves to being automated more readily than others but it is difficult to rank them in any preferred order because there are so many options open to the production engineer within the process or method chosen. However, as a general guide a list is given overleaf together with some general comments on the technique used.

Assembly operation	Comments
PRESS FIT	Provide good initial lead-in on both parts and keep tight control over tolerances. Check that differential expansion will not cause fretting between surfaces which can loosen the assembly. Prevent weak materials from splitting by putting them in compression. Ensure materials will not creep and loosen parts. Ensure different materials cannot set up electrolytic corrosion.
STAKING	Wood or other soft material used as a base for clasps, rails or cleats which can be fired through thin side of hard material if required.
WELDING	A wide choice of equipment exists depending on the application ranging from butt, spot, friction, arc and gas welding for similar metals and ultrasonic welding for plastics. Butt welding is an effective way of providing a continuous material feed into an assembly machine where a cropping operation provides the feed in the machine and avoids the need to bowl-feed or magazine the parts, such as pins or wire, that could be difficult to feed or become damaged. Spot Welding is the most common means of creating welded assemblies automatically because the spots do not require a high accuracy of placement and the work is presented between the weld heads using similar equipment to that of the manual worker. If the automated equipment is built around the original welder then its ability to withstand the new duty cycle required will have to be checked. Where the spots required cannot be presented to the welding heads, such as with car bodies, the welding heads can be programmed to move round the assembly. Failure to obtain good results can be caused by poor maintenance of the weld tips which should be kept clean to prevent them sticking to the assembly when excessive current is drawn. Arc welding is another area where robots with continuous path control can be programmed to carry out various tasks, but investigations are still proceeding to make this method cope with the wide variation of component tolerances usually found, and the problem of slag removal still exists. In Ultrasonic welding the weld occurs where the plastic touches. This eliminates the need for a high degree of accuracy on the part of the welder but places the onus on well-designed mating faces of the plastics parts. The assembly can be brought together automatically under a previously manually-fed welder provided it can cope with the new duty cycle.
RIVETING	Various types of rivets are available which cover most combinations of materials. These include: 1. Bifurcated rivets for piercing soft materials that do not split and need no special alignment. 2. Solid rivets where extra work is required to produce rivet holes which require accurate alignment between adjacent holes and a good accuracy of rivet placement. Used on strong materials that will not crush or split.

Assembly operation	Comments
RIVETING *continued*	3. Blind rivets where access is only needed from one side of the assembly. In certain circumstances these can be used in blind holes of soft material. Correct choice of materials should be made to avoid electrolytic corrosion.
BRAZING	Brazing and silver-soldering slugs can be placed automatically together with parts that can be fed into a furnance or rotated between gas jets.
SCREWING	Cheapest screw assembly can be made with wood screw or self-tapping screw, as they only require one or two extra holes to be drilled and tend to be self-aligning. Although automated screw drivers are produced for all types of head the best types are those which take a star drive because the screw tends to have a more reliable head shape. Set screws and bolts come with a variety of heads and the above comments on star-type drives still hold good. If screw drive slots must be used, nylon moulded screws usually have a better quality head. Supplying nuts for these fasteners is not always easy because of variations in the nut shape and it is better if one component is tapped. The drilling and tapping process being incorporated on the assembly machine can also help reduce the high accuracy of part placement that would otherwise be required. Most automated screwdrivers can be adjusted to give consistent torque settings.
BENDING	Metals assembled in this way require extra forming of the original material by modifying the press tools to produce slots and tabs or twin folds along edges. Unsuitable for brittle materials or those likely to set up electrolytic corrosion.
SPRINGING	Most types of materials can be assembled with one of the many types of fasteners available. Some of these fasteners are very difficult to feed automatically because they interlock. They are ideal for parts which are intended to come apart again where some degree of freedom, space saving, material saving, or savings in machining are required. Typical devices include fasteners like circlips for metals and snap connectors which are widely used in plastics where they can be produced in one piece mouldings.
PINNING	These fastening techniques are used with most materials and include straight, taper and cotter pinning. Additional machining is required to receive the pins. See "press fit" for other remarks.
BONDING	Wide choice available to suit most materials. Different curing rates can also be found as well as different conditions under which the action will start. Although parts can then be handled some time may elapse before full strength is reached. Careful control over the conditions under which adhesives are applied, together with education of the labour

Assembly operation	Comments
BONDING *continued*	force, is necessary to obtain the correct results. This may entail using special metering apparatus and wearing protective clothing. Adhesives may also be used as sealants. Automatic inspection is difficult and checks on the assembly for strength and pressure leaks may have to be made.
STITCHING	Fabrics usually require a large amount of manual dexterity to control input and output to work heads. Some automatic work can be carried out by stitching fabric over removable templates or by moving sewing head.

CHAPTER 3

AUTOMATED ASSEMBLY: DEVELOPING THE MACHINE

INTRODUCTION

This chapter is not intended to be a technical guide which explains how to design machines or even how to select equipment. It is intended to help the manager to appreciate the options available and to draw his attention to some of the problems he may encounter.

In deciding to automate a process it will first be necessary to ensure that:

- the product is viable and will have a reasonable life in the market-place
- the product is capable of assembly by mechanical techniques
- the total cost of automating the process is justified, whether on economic grounds alone or for some other reason such as shortage of labour, process hazards of the need for consistent quality
- the necessary skills to operate and maintain the proposed machinery at an acceptable level of efficiency are available or can be obtained
- the proposed changes are likely to be acceptable to the labour force.

The feasibility studies will have indicated the likely problem areas and a process flow-sheet will have been prepared specifying the assembly procedure, the process layout, the overall requirements for the individual machine or machines in the lay-out and where manual operations, if any, are necessary. The flow-sheet may indicate also the need for buffer storage between machines, inspection points, off-line component or sub-assembly manufacture, in-feed systems or possibly packaging. It is now necessary to concentrate on the design and development of the automated assembly process.

STAGES IN DEVELOPMENT

The effective design and development of an automated assembly machine generally results from a process which can be illustrated by the cycle shown overleaf (Fig. 3).

This cycle shows:

- the interdependence of the product and the process
- the fact that development will be required during and after the build

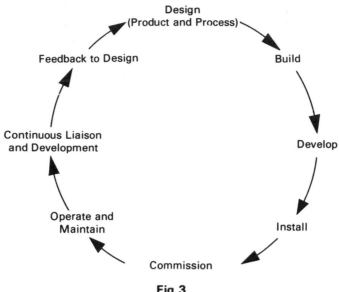

Design
(Product and Process)

Build

Develop

Install

Commission

Operate and
Maintain

Continuous Liaison
and Development

Feedback to Design

Fig 3

- that the machine will require commissioning after installation. At this stage it may also be necessary to make further modifications to the product to achieve the desired production efficiencies

- that assembly machines often require further development after commissioning and when in production

- that the design and development staff should maintain a continuous liaison with production personnel to ensure that the design specifications and drawings are up-dated. This is essential if further machinery is to be ordered.

The whole approach to the design and selection of equipment has, therefore, to be practical, bearing in mind always that the object is to achieve reliability and efficient production *on the shop floor.*

Depending on the particular company practice, the rig work and the initial design may commence before financial approval for the project is obtained. However, the activities of design, selection of proprietary equipment and rig work are often carried out in parallel. Certainly, it pays in terms of overall project time to order long lead-time items as soon as possible after specifications for them are finalised.

Early in the design work the user must specify his requirements in terms of metric or English dimensions. Unfortunately, metrication is a problem which has still been tackled only partially in British engineering companies. It may therefore be necessary to compromise because an assembly machine is usually a special purpose machine utilising many proprietary items. However, the user should determine the standards in this respect.

The design of assembly machines is considerably eased if it is intended to make one product only and if that product is destined to have some years life in the market place. It is possible, however, to design machines capable of adjustment or capable of accepting change parts to make similar products, e.g. one can often cater easily for a change in size where the general design of the product is unchanged. It is also possible in some cases to build machines so that when a particular product is no longer required the modules can be used again in building a machine for some other product. Experience indicates that the most successful assembly machines, in terms of reliability and efficiency in production, have been built with one specific product in mind.

Designers, whether employed in-company or outside, are in business to attract design work. They are also very interested in achieving success with their machines on the shop floor, but the user manager—whether Project Manager, Factory Manager, Production Manager or Engineering Manager—owes it to himself and to his company to ensure that he gets what he wants. He must ensure that the degree of mechanisation envisaged is indeed feasible and that the designer's proposals have a very good chance of success.

From the production point of view he must accept that machines do break down and that the more complex the machine, the more likely it will be to break down. Simplicity usually pays off later and it is best to use proven techniques wherever possible. He must avoid too, the situation where he has "all his eggs in one basket"—it is often better to avoid the use of one larger or high-speed machine in favour of two smaller or slower machines.

MACHINE DESIGN

The size and weight of the product assembly will determine the size and weight of the machine or machines and the standards of engineering adopted will be influenced by the usage—whether single, double or triple shift—the type of labour employed, and the overall costs incurred.

In the interests of reliability and efficiency the number of workheads and placement devices per machine should be minimised. There is no hard and fast rule here, but it must be appreciated that each assembly function on the machine depends on the dimensional accuracy and consistency of the components and the consistent operation of a feeder, an orientation device, an escapement and a placement device. It is not surprising, therefore, that the overall efficiency of each assembly function is usually less than 100%. Moreover, an assembly machine is likely to consist of one or more assembly stations linked by and synchronised with some transfer or conveyor system. The overall efficiency of such a machine is determined by the arithmetic multiplication of the individual efficiencies of each assembly function. It should therefore be accepted that much higher efficiencies are likely to be achieved by machines which assemble together only 2 or 3 components.

The designer has much historical information at his disposal together with advice from colleagues, suppliers, various institutions and associations.

He will probably start his work by selecting or designing the various feed systems, magazines, escapements, parts-placing mechanisms for each assembly function. All of these should be capable of similar or greater speeds than the desired overall machine speed.

The designer will then consider the work carrier or nest and decide how this is to be transferred or conveyed. The work carriers or nests may be queued and moved from assembly station to assembly station or they may be fitted to jigs or platens, which themselves are attached in a fixed or floating manner to chains or belts of various types or they may be designed in as a permanent feature on the machine, e.g. on a turret type of machine.

The decision as to whether to assemble continuously or on an indexing machine and as to whether the conveying method should be linear or rotary will usually have been made at the feasibility stage. The choice of linear versus rotary is often one of opinion but it cannot be divorced from the choice of continuous versus indexing motion, although some operations are impossible to carry out on continuous motion systems. The choice should be made on the basis of:

(i) process feasibility

(ii) accuracy of placing required—precision of stopping can be very important. The effect of the acceleration and deceleration characteristics of indexing mechanisms on the product should be considered and the possibility of chain stretch must be borne in mind

(iii) plant layout

(iv) operator ergonomics

(v) access for maintenance.

There is no doubt, however, that higher speeds are attainable more easily on continuous motion machines.

The designer must give careful attention to the drives, power requirements and control systems, e.g. electrical and electronic, pneumatic, hydraulic. In the early stages of machine development it can be helpful to fit a variable speed main drive of more than adequate power, for however good the designer may be at predicting speed and overall power requirements, it is more than likely in practice that a change will have to be made in the course of the project.

Experience suggests that it is best to determine the optimum operating speed in production and calculate the power usage by actual amperage readings. If it is necessary to fix the speed before handing over to production operators, this can be arranged and a motor with the correct power characteristics can be provided.

The type of power and control systems to be employed must be determined early in the project, because they so often influence the overall layout of the machine. When defining power and control systems the following should be borne in mind:

● workheads may have safety features designed in but it is essential to include torque-limiting devices, clutch/brake assemblies or "over current" trip-out devices in the main drive system. The drive itself will usually be a motor/gear-box with suitable output speed and torque characteristics but with machines of large inertia it may be necessary to include fluid couplings, hydraulic gear-boxes or torque converters to provide a gradual start-up

● as part of the assembly process itself it may be necessary to check that a machine function has been completed before the next function can commence or that a component has been correctly placed before the next component is placed, or that incorrect partial assemblies or complete assemblies are rejected. It may also be important to stop the machine should one station run out of components or have an insufficient head of components to maintain a reasonable feed

- it may be necessary to slow down one machine until another catches up. This may be done by providing buffer stock and then either slowing down or speeding up machines or holding back partial assemblies. The latter method is used on production lines where a number of machines are inter-linked. In such cases some machines are "product initiated", i.e. they only operate when a predetermined level of components is available

- it is common practice today to include enunciation (coloured light indicators or alarms) to indicate when the machine stops and to indicate to the operator where the particular fault has occurred

Obviously, too, the designer must provide a suitable main frame or support system and this will be needed early in the build phase. Other auxiliaries such as overhead platforms or access platforms may also be required.

Further, inspection processes may be required at critical points in the assembly and on completion of the assembly. These may involve electrical tests of various kinds, dimensional checks, pressure or strength tests.

The whole process should be satisfactory from the operator ergonomic point of view, ease of and access for maintenance, and last but not least, the safety of the operators and sometimes the safety and protection of the completed assemblies. Where possible, too, equipment should not produce noise above acceptable levels. If there is a problem, then suitable noise control methods should be devised.

Having catered for all these items the designer must still try to achieve an overall machine design which is clean in line and, if possible, with some aesthetic appeal.

PREDICTING MACHINE PERFORMANCE

Predicting machine speeds is not an exact science. It depends very much on the experience of designers who have been concerned with similar products. With light or simple assemblies, speeds may vary from say 30 per minute up to say 600 per minute or higher. Under 30 per minute the assembly may be carried out more economically by manual methods. Heavy or complicated assemblies will inevitably be carried out at lower speeds. However, the designer will usually be able to predict whether his machine will run at 10, 20, 50 or say 100 items per minute. He will base his estimate on his knowledge of the process compared with other processes of a similar nature with which he has been involved. Certainly he will be influenced by the rig work he has carried out and whether the machine operates in a continuous or intermittent manner.

Having established the likely machine speed the likely machine efficiency must also be predicted. To arrive at this it is necessary to make an assessment of the component feed efficiency, each individual workhead efficiency, and the transfer mechanism or conveyor efficiency and by multiplication obtain the theoretical machine efficiency.

Unfortunately assembly machines can break down and they are sensitive to poor quality components and to careless operators and maintenance staff. The true practical machine efficiency will be lower than the theoretical for these reasons. However, the practical machine efficiency needs to be maintained by ensuring that adequate supplies of good components are provided at all times. In some circumstances 100% pre-checking or pre-selection of certain components may be justified to ensure continuous running of the assembly machine.

As indicated earlier the provision of magazines or buffer stock between workheads or between individual machines can improve overall efficiencies. It is also highly desirable to provide the means for rapid access into feed chutes or escapements etc., so that offending or jammed components can be removed quickly.

Only in the most simple assembly processes do production rates reach 80-90% of the theoretical. 65-70% is more common at this stage of development.

Generally speaking, providing the design is right, the life and reliability of a machine will improve with cost. Overall production efficiency, however, is quite a different thing in that whilst it obviously depends on machine efficiency, it is also influenced by the quality of components and by the calibre of the operators and maintenance staff. Production efficiency is thus very much in the hands of the manager.

CHAPTER 4

AUTOMATED ASSEMBLY: THE CONTROL OF QUALITY

INTRODUCTION

In addition to the major benefits such as cost reduction and increased throughput, another factor which may influence the decision to automate assembly is the scope for achieving higher and more consistent quality of the completed assembly. Even if there is no great need to improve on quality levels the introduction of automated assembly may well be discredited if the quality of the assemblies produced falls significantly below that previously obtained by manual methods.

It is important that the whole question of quality performance should be examined well before the introduction of a new assembly machine. It inevitably takes time to achieve and sustain improvements in component quality and if this vital aspect of automated assembly is ignored until the stage of commissioning the new machine, it is very possible that the acceptance by Production of the machine could be delayed by several months because of operational problems caused by poor and inconsistent component quality. This chapter suggests some ways in which this vital question should be tackled.

QUALITY ASSURANCE OF COMPONENTS

The assembly machine will have been designed to handle and perform assembly operations on components of a given specification. The machine may well be made to operate effectively with these components, but if the assembly operations performed are intricate and precise, the operational efficiency of the machine as a production unit is very likely to depend more than anything else on the conformance to specification of the components that are subsequently fed into it.

In those cases where components have to be re-designed in order to provide features which aid assembly the problem of quality control is likely to be less than in cases where the assembly operation is carried out with components that may have been designed some years previously. In the latter circumstances it is first essential to check current production against the original drawings and specifications. This check may well reveal that some components are no longer made to the original specification because, over a period of years, it is likely that official (and possibly some unofficial!) concessions in relation to dimensions, tolerances and finishes will have been made without recording all the details on the drawing.

This situation can give rise to a great number of potential quality problems if it is not approached in a positive and firm manner. The first step is to ensure the correct specification of all components to be included in the assembly operation and then have new updated drawings produced. This can be a time-consuming and detailed procedure involving Product Design, Planning, Inspection and Production, but it is essential that it is done. The problem of achieving good and consistent component quality is not easy and it is most unlikely to be achieved if those concerned with quality, i.e. standards, production, inspection and quality assurance, are not quite clear and agreed about what should be produced in the first place!

Once the problem of component specification has been resolved the next step is to check the quality of production against these specifications. In this respect the quality level can be defined as the extent to which the characteristics (i.e. dimensions and finish) of the manufactured components conform to the specification. In doing this it is important to check production comprehensively by sampling batches produced by different shifts, machine tools and operators. If these checks reveal wide variations in the degree of conformance, it will probably be necessary to institute new quality control methods. These methods will vary depending upon the type of component and the method of manufacture but for machined components they would probably involve the use of techniques such as modern sampling plans and pre-control. The latter is a technique which involves machining to tolerances within the specified figures (usually about two thirds) thereby providing the operator or setter with the opportunity to take the necessary action in making adjustments before the dimensions drift beyond the required tolerances. Pre-control is based on statistical theory and, when applied to automated machines, it greatly reduces the incidence of dimensionally incorrect components within a batch.

The introduction of these quality controls may well reveal that it is difficult to maintain high quality levels with existing methods of manufacture. In these circumstances it will be necessary to experiment with alternatives, and perhaps introduce different machining methods or use jigs and fixtures. The revision of these manufacturing methods will take time and might even increase the cost of producing the component but, bearing in mind that the life of the assembly machine is likely to be several years, it is obviously important to minimise potential future problems by establishing manufacturing methods which will consistently produce components of the desired quality.

The quality checks described above should also be extended to standard components such as nuts, bolts, screws, etc. The uniformity of these components tends to be taken for granted but they frequently cause jamming of assembly machines. It is important that typical faults such as cross-threads, no threads, variations in shank length and head thickness, and missing screw head slots be kept to a minimum.

The drive to improve quality should also include bought-out components. It is generally unwise to assume that the quality of purchased components will automatically be good and a detailed check on the quality of a component supplied by different vendors frequently reveals a wide variation in the degree of conformance. There are several vendor rating systems which can be used to check the level and consistency of component quality from different sources and these are useful in determining who are the most reliable suppliers. In practice, however, the best way of achieving improvements in the quality of purchased components is to send the supplier a detailed drawing/specification informing him that conformance against the drawing will be checked by using a specified sampling plan and that if the batch fails this quality check it will be returned to him. In these circumstances the supplier may well ensure that this sampling plan is applied to batches of the components before they are despatched.

Although every attempt must be made to improve component quality before the introduction of a new assembly machine, it is realistic to accept that all quality control systems have limitations for economic reasons and that some faulty components will be fed into the machine. Although the machine will probably accept some components that are not within drawing limits, others will cause jamming or some malfunction and it is important that these faulty components be identified. However, good parts can also cause jamming for a variety of reasons. Rather than inspect and gauge each part that causes a jam or stoppage, it is frequently more sensible to mark the part that jams, return it to the vibratory bowl and check whether it re-appears as the cause of a stoppage. If it does cause another jam the part should be gauged to determine which dimensions are outside limits and the details should be recorded. By logging this information each time a stoppage due to a faulty component occurs it will be possible to establish the component dimensions that are critical for effective performance of the machine and these can then be controlled more rigidly during manufacture.

In addition to controlling component dimensions it may also be necessary to ensure reasonable consistency of surface finish of these components. Vibratory bowl feeders and some output tracks rely on gravity and their performance is dependent on friction. Changes in component finish which might result from the introduction of different manufacturing methods (i.e. from turning to grinding or from machining to casting or from different plating processes) could have a significant effect on machine performance. Here again, it is important to log all the details whenever stoppages occur and establish the critical characteristics in relation to the surface finish of components.

Another important requirement for efficient automated assembly is good housekeeping and general cleanliness. If components are produced in a dirty or greasy state a cleaning operation is likely to be essential if the contamination level of the product and the automatic feed mechanism cannot be controlled. Foreign matter such as swarf, scrap and dirt can cause stoppages, and possibly damage, if they get into feed tracks and work stations. These potential problems can be reduced by regular cleaning of the machine and checking the input to the vibratory bowls.

As a prerequisite to introducing an assembly machine it is frequently necessary to redesign components and tighten up quality control. However, if good quality control techniques are introduced and then practised the components will be more easily assembled manually than they were before. This generally results in higher or better quality output by manual assembly methods in addition to providing an essential requirement for the eventual introduction of automated assembly.

QUALITY ASSURANCE OF MACHINE OUTPUT

The quality of output from an assembly machine can drop below the level obtained with manual assembly because of the way in which parts are handled mechanically and the inability of the machine to pick out minor defects that would be easily identified by manual workers. It is therefore important to ensure effective quality control of the machine output.

Any suspect assembly machine methods should be tried before the machine is commissioned; for example, bowl feeding of parts to manual assembly stations will show whether this method gives rise to damaged parts.

Precautions can be taken against the scuffing of components by lining grippers, escapement mechanisms and feeder tracks with softer materials. Barrelling of parts in bulk feeders can be reduced by coating the feeder but the damage caused by the interaction of components with each other is more difficult to overcome. It can be reduced by keeping a minimum store in the feeder and handling as many components as possible from the flight track using external means to orientate the components. As a final resort parts may have to be hand-placed into the assembly machine from an operator-paced station. Further damage can be caused by incorrect settings on the assembly machine giving poor positioning and handling of components.

Quality control of the output of the assembly machine must be rigorously practiced with a true sense of economics. If deformed components do get into the machine they can result in some malfunctioning of the machine and every effort should be made to detect this as early as possible. Automatic checks of the part being fed into the machine are very useful but can be expensive. Another option is to allow the machine to jam, but as a final safeguard frequent inspection of the output should be made.

Missing parts due to machine malfunction or lack of supply, although serious, should not necessarily stop the assembly process. Providing access is available it may be cheaper to add the missing part by hand at a more convenient time to enable the machine to continue its cycle. Some assembly machines provide the facility to switch out a station and, in these cases, the offending station can be by-passed and an operator put into the line to maintain the assembly sequence.

If the assembly is likely to trap swarf or scrap which may be produced during the assembly operation, e.g. by piercing or drilling, then open floor output chutes should be employed which encourage the assembly to tumble as much as possible before it is discharged into a bin. However, some final assemblies may be damaged by dropping them at the machine output station. In order to avoid such damage the machine output can be arranged to form the assemblies into a queue which can be dealt with by an operator; alternatively, the assemblies can be mechanically pushed out of the machine into a set pattern or onto a conveyor.

Although certain aspects of quality control may need tightening up before installing as assembly machine the additional costs involved should be balanced against increased output and reduced labour involvement. In circumstances where there is no apparent benefit, such as in the case of detailed manual inspection of a screen printing process before assembly, the use of a machine may still be justified economically by magazining the printed part after inspection.

It should also be stressed that if components can be assembled in more than one way a manual worker will occasionally make the mistake of doing so, but machines can be made to avoid this possibility where it is imperative that this should not happen, i.e. an assembly used in safety apparatus which must work the first time it is used.

AUTOMATIC INSPECTION

An assembly machine can be designed to carry out automatic inspection in order to check:

- features on a component that may cause the assembly machine to stop or jam
- features that are vital to the assembly of the components
- that the component will perform correctly after assembly
- whether components have been assembled
- that the assembly is functioning properly.

Automatic inspection adds to the cost of an assembly machine by increasing the complexity of the mechanisms and control devices, and in certain cases it can affect the output rate of the machine. It is possible to check whether the part is in place at the pick-up station or on the assembly using pressure, proximity, photocell or probe devices. These devices can also be used to check on certain component features before assembly. Recently, more accurate checks on a wider range of component features have been made possible by the developing use of lasers, checking-threads and visual techniques which facilitate inspection in two dimensions.

The use of automatic inspection will influence the way in which parts that fail the test need to be treated. Providing that there is an adequate supply of parts automatic rejection of the part before assembly should allow the machine to continue without a reduction in output or quality. However, if an assembly is checked at a machine station and found to be incorrect a decision to allow the faulty assembly through to the next station or the output stage may be better than stopping the machine to allow an operator to remove the offending part. The provision of additional mechanisms to carry out the removal function at this stage may be prohibitively expensive but an additional check at the output stage could ensure that the faulty assembly is discharged into a separate bin.

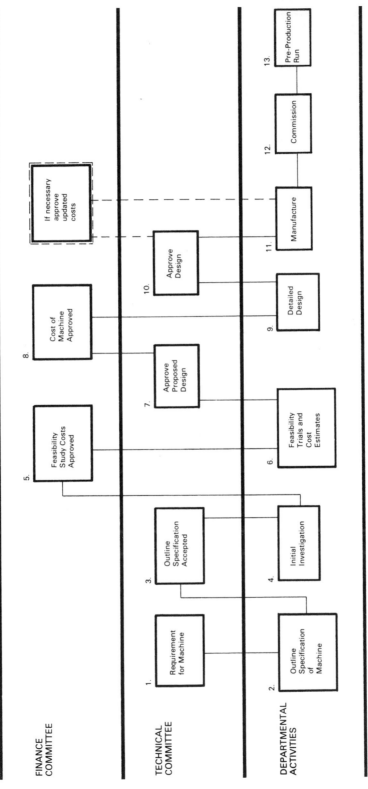

STAGES IN PROJECT TO INTRODUCE AN AUTOMATED ASSEMBLY MACHINE

FINANCE COMMITTEE

5. Feasibility Study Costs Approved

8. Cost of Machine Approved

If necessary approve updated costs

TECHNICAL COMMITTEE

3. Outline Specification Accepted

7. Approve Proposed Design

10. Approve Design

DEPARTMENTAL ACTIVITIES

1. Requirement for Machine

2. Outline Specification of Machine

4. Initial Investigation

6. Feasibility Trials and Cost Estimates

9. Detailed Design

11. Manufacture

12. Commission

13. Pre-Production Run

Fig 4

CHAPTER 5

THE INTRODUCTION OF AUTOMATED ASSEMBLY: PROJECT MANAGEMENT

INTRODUCTION

The introduction of some form of automated assembly is normally an exercise which involves most of the functions in a company—Design, Product Development, Marketing, Manufacturing Engineering, Finance and Production. The initial requirement for automated assembly may be modified or extended as a result of marketing or design influences. The production engineers may well have to compromise between sophistication and simplicity because of costs and practical operational considerations. The pre-production run will almost certainly reveal needs for further modifications and possibly additional costs. In view of all these interdependent factors, the introduction of even a comparatively simple form of automated assembly should be regarded as a project which needs to be carefully controlled from inception until the new machine is functioning to the satisfaction of all concerned. This chapter outlines the main stages in such a project.

FUNCTION INVOLVED IN PROJECTS

The way in which an automated assembly project is tackled will vary enormously depending upon the size and organisational structure of the particular company. However, the main corporate functions involved in the decision making will inevitably be financial and technical and the project will be progressed through a sequence of activities undertaken by different departments in the company. This process is illustrated in Fig. 4 which charts the stages of a typical project and indicates the financial and technical functions by reference to committees. The composition of these committees will clearly vary from company to company. In a small firm the Finance Committee may be the Chief Accountant alone, or the Managing Director, and the Technical Committee may be the Chief Engineer. In a large firm the Finance Committee could be the Board of Directors or a sub-committee set up by the Board, and the Technical Committee might comprise the heads of the Engineering, Production, Design and Marketing Departments.

If a machine is to progress speedily into production it is essential to have one person fully responsible for the project and this person can sensibly be described as the Project Engineer. In a small firm he may be the one and only engineer; in a medium firm a planning or production engineer; in a larger firm one of a number of engineers employed solely to produce special purpose machines.

It is advisable to use some form of chart with which to monitor progress. This may vary from a PERT network if the machine is complicated or, if several machines are being progressed concurrently, to a simple GANTT bar chart for monitoring the progress of a simple machine*.

STAGES IN PROJECT

The chart given in Fig. 4 shows 13 main stages in a project to introduce an automated assembly machine. These stages are not all necessarily sequential and some may proceed concurrently, but they are all essential and are briefly described below:

1. Requirement for Machine

The usual reason for considering automation is to achieve cost savings. However, other considerations can make it desirable to automate, such as the inability to obtain staff in times of full employment. It may therefore be of benefit, even though there are no cost savings, to automate suitable operations so that staff can be freed to work on operations which cannot be automated. A job may be unpleasant or difficult so that staff may object or even refuse to do it, and in these conditions automation may well provide the answer.

2. Agree Outline Specification for Machine

The Project Engineer will list the objectives to be achieved by the proposed machine. These objectives must be clearly defined and should include a list of components to be assembled, drawings of components and sub-assemblies; the quantities required per week, some assessment of the time the assembly is expected to remain in production, and the location of the final machine.

3. Outline Specification Studied and Accepted

The outline specification will be submitted to the Technical Committee for approval. If agreed, authority will be given to proceed to the initial investigation stage.

4. Initial Investigation

The Project Engineer should call a meeting of representatives of all the interested departments, such as the product and tool design departments, inspection department, engineering department, and the manager of the shop which will run the machine. If an existing assembly operation is to be automated the manager of the shop in which the operation is at present carried out should also be present to give advice on the existing problems and special know-how required. This group should discuss such matters as:

- the general principles for the design of the machine, i.e. whether it should be a rotary machine, in-line machine etc.

---

*For those not conversant with these charts there is some useful information in a Pitman publication "An Introduction to Critical Path Analysis" by K. G. Lockyer.

- whether it would be safer to have two machines each with half the required capacity to give some cover in the case of breakdown
- the basic method of feeding
- general problem areas—of which some may need to be overcome by redesign of the product (e.g. a screwed fixing changed to a press fixing).

The Inspection Department can indicate the actual conditions of components which may differ from those stated on drawings, i.e. agreed concessions on dimensional tolerances, finish etc. Some differences may not be known, because they do not affect the function of the product, or interfere with manual assembly. It is therefore essential to check all components to find out exactly what is being produced.

At this stage the Project Engineer should have enough information to decide if it is necessary to carry out any further studies on problem areas which may be expected with either the product or the machine. For example, there may have been some changes proposed to the product in order to simplify or cheapen assembly. In this case it is essential to make components and carry out thorough testing to ensure that the redesigned product still performs its function satisfactorily. On the machine itself there may be some components which would be difficult to feed, or some difficult process to carry out. Here again it will be necessary to make some simple mock-ups to prove these points.

A preliminary layout of the machine should be produced showing the outline size of the machine, the position of the stations and position of feed units, stating the function performed at each station and which part is being fed. A typical layout is shown in Fig. 5 (overleaf).

The Project Engineer should then complete a short report outlining the feasibility studies he wishes to carry out, with estimated costs of these studies and submit these, together with the outline drawing, to the Finance Committee.

5. Feasibility Study Cost Approval

If the Finance Committee approve the money to be spent on the feasibility study they will issue the necessary authority to proceed.

6. Feasibility Trials and Cost Estimates

The Project Engineer will arrange for any necessary parts to be made so that he can try out his ideas and be fairly well assured that there is a good chance of the particular difficulties being overcome. He should then be in a position to make a reasonable estimate of the cost of the proposed machine, and have a good idea as to whether the quantities required can be produced from one machine, or whether more than one will be needed, bearing in mind the possible efficiency of the machine. For estimating costs and production quantities the machine efficiency would probably be assessed at between 50% and 70%, depending on the complexity of the machine. This figure may seem low and many machines do run at higher efficiencies, but high efficiency should be considered as a bonus and not counted on at the costing stage.

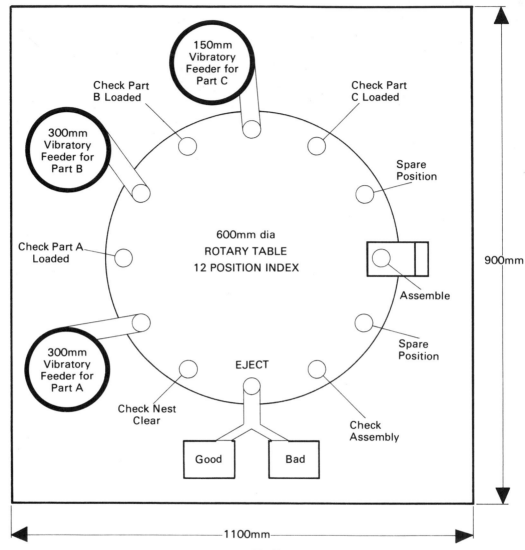

Fig 5

The costing for the machine, plus the cost of any operator to run it, should be tabulated alongside the cost of the present assembly method. Other factors which might influence the introduction of the machine should be quoted; for example, it may be that the product could be assembled at a very high speed thereby reducing lead times, or the consistency of quality of the product may be improved as a result of 100% checking built into the machine.

This information will be passed to the Technical Committee.

7. Approve Proposed Design of the Machine

The Technical Committee would study the rough layout and the results of the feasibility studies with a view to approving the proposed design of the machine. If approved, the cost data will be passed to the Finance Committee.

8. Approve Cost of Machine

The Finance Committee will consider the likely capital cost of the machine, the comparative costs of existing and proposed assembly methods and the life of the product or products assembled. If the benefits arising from the successful implementation of this new assembly process are satisfactory, they will issue authority to proceed with the detailed design stage. If the proposed machine is complex and likely to be expensive the Finance Committee may sanction a fund or specify the amount to be spent on the design, development and build of the machine.

9. Detailed Design

Detailed design, which may be carried out internally or by an outside vendor, is a very important stage and the Project Engineer must keep in close contact with the design section to ensure the speedy resolution of any problems which may arise. It is very likely that some of the ideas proposed on the original layout will not work out in detail and that different solutions to problems are necessary. In addition to the detailed design of the assembly machine it is important at this stage to consider the following:

Accessibility

There should be a reasonable amount of room around the various stations for ease of access because even with simple machines there are likely to be stops caused by misfeed, faulty components, and jamming of assembly heads. These stops must be expected and will not cause any serious problem if the offending parts can be cleared quickly. However, if the machine is too compact and a number of pieces have to be removed to obtain effective access, the cumulative effects of such disruptions can be very serious. For example, if five different components are being fed each at 99% efficiency to a machine with a three-second cycle (one every 3 sec = 20 per min = 100 per 5 min), it will be seen that each feed would, on average, stop at five minutes intervals. Therefore, with five parts the machine would on average stop every minute and even if it took only 30 seconds to clear each stop, the overall machine efficiency would be reduced dramatically.

Protection of the machine from damage

If a machine is powered by an electric motor, a torque-limiting device must be added to protect the machine in case of overload. It is also a good idea, where possible, to make assembling mechanisms and inserters spring-loaded to avoid damage if parts are incorrectly fed etc. Interlocks should be included to ensure that the indexing mechanisms cannot operate until assembly heads are fully returned.

Safety of the operator and persons near the machine

Since the introduction of the Health and Safety Act it is even more than ever essential that machines are adequately guarded, with the necessary interlocks which will render the machine inoperative if guards are removed. If bowl feeding is used it is usual to leave them outside the guarding as they are quite safe and allow the operator access for topping up the bowls and for removing any blockages which may occur. Where possible, electrical circuits should be contained in a control box. The box should be automatically isolated from the mains supply when it is opened*.

Once the detailed design of the machine has been finalised, all the details together with updated costings and other relevant information about component changes and inspection procedures must be submitted to the Technical Committee for final approval.

10. Approve Design

The Technical Committee will study the detailed design and, if satisfied and providing the financial benefits are within those originally envisaged, will issue authority to proceed with manufacture. However, if the revised costs are significantly above those originally agreed, they must be re-submitted to the Finance Committee for approval.

The introduction of the proposed new machine will almost certainly have implications on the shop floor in terms of manning levels and possibly operator skills. At the stage when the design of the machine has been approved it is important to have detailed discussions with the workers' representatives with a view to resolving any potential labour problems which could prevent the smooth introduction of the machine into production. These discussions will, of course, deal with such matters as the redeployment of displaced labour, the training of operators for the new machine and their payment arrangements. If tackled at this early time, it is likely that negotiations will be easier, as the workers will know that they are being involved at an early stage; this approach would avoid the confrontation situation that is almost certain to arise if the machine were to be installed without consultation.

In a company considering automated assembly for the first time it would be advisable to have preliminary talks with workers' representatives to outline the general approach and the implications as soon as it is possible to do so. In an expanding company it might be possible to assure workers that there will be no redundancies and that people will be redeployed on other work. If, however, redundancies are inevitable it is better to start dealing with this problem at the earliest possible stage.

11. Manufacture

The manufacture of the machine may be done within the company, by an outside vendor or by some combination of both. In any case, detailed quotations should be obtained for the manufacture, and detailed checks should be made with the original costings, to ensure that they correspond with the estimates, otherwise further approval may be necessary.

Most outside vendors will give a firm quotation for manufacture of the machine as specified. However, it is much more difficult to specify the time and

---

*In considering safety implications it is useful to consult recent publications such as the British Standards Institute Code of Practice for Safeguarding of Machinery (BS 5304:1975) or the Management Guide to Health and Safety at Work published by The Institution of Production Engineers.

costs required for commissioning and should the vendor be asked to quote for the actual commissioning of the machine, it is essential to agree with him target costs which must not be exceeded without further authority. This approach enables the Project Engineer to decide whether he will accept the machine with the sub-optimum efficiency so far achieved, or whether he should persuade the Finance Committee to spend more to achieve better results; in the latter case the maximum sum to be spent must again be specified, otherwise costs can run out of hand in an effort to achieve the optimum performance.

During manufacture the Project Engineer should make regular visits to ensure that the machine is proceeding satisfactorily, and that any queries which may arise are speedily dealt with.

12. Commissioning

The commissioning stage involves working on the machine to ensure that it is made capable of producing a consistent standard suitable for production. This stage is usually controlled by the Project Engineer who will, of course, have a complete knowledge of what the machine should do. He should also ensure that drawings are updated to show any changes he may have to make to the machine.

Trial runs may well indicate that it would be well worthwhile to tighten up a tolerance on a component or indeed modify a component in order to ensure high machine efficiency even though these changes may not be important to the function of the product.

During the commissioning stage the Project Engineer will be faced with the problem of deciding when further work on the machine cannot be financially justified. In doing this he must weigh up the money already spent, the likely further cost related to potential improvements, the efficiency originally estimated, the level of cost savings, the promise the machine shows, the time already spent in relation to the probable life of the product—all of which will have a bearing on his decision.

During the commissioning of the machine, the Project Engineer should make a list of spares which may be required. He should also specify for the operator/setter the method of operating the machine, i.e. sequence of switching on feed bowls, motor, air, hydraulics, etc., and also list any regular servicing which should be carried out, i.e. greasing, oiling, topping up of hydraulics, etc. He should ensure that, wherever possible, circuit drawings for all the electric, pneumatic and hydraulic equipment are fixed to the machines. It is also advisable to list the exact sequence of operations of the machine.

13. Pre-production Run

When the Project Engineer is confident that the machine is running reasonably well, the permanent operator and setter selected for the machine should be introduced to it and trained by the person commissioning the machine. The manager and/or foreman of the shop taking over the machine should also spend as much time as possible familiarising himself with the machine.

During this pre-production run it is useful to log all stoppages, specifying the reason and the period of time that elapses before re-starting so that the potential trouble areas on which the operator will need to concentrate can be highlighted.

THE IMPORTANCE OF PROJECT MANAGEMENT

Because of the potential benefits that can arise from the introduction of automated assembly there is always the danger that companies will rush into it without proper planning and control with the result that the project gets out of hand and is subsequently discredited. Furthermore, it is very easy to overspend on a project because of the natural tendency for the engineers involved in the project to seek perfection in arriving at the answers to the problems which will inevitably occur.

These difficulties can be avoided by following the steps described in this chapter. In particular, it is essential that the potential value of the project be questioned at various stages. The costings prepared at the outline specification stage must therefore be checked at the design stage, rechecked during the manufacturing stage and carefully monitored during the commissioning stage.

This chapter has shown that the project management of a new assembly machine can be a complex and major activity. However, the introduction of automated assembly means much more than the design, development and commissioning of a machine. It can have an important influence on product design, component production methods and inspection techniques and thus has implications for many people—both management and work force—who are not directly involved in the specific assembly operation which is being automated. Successful introduction of automated assembly must therefore depend not only on engineering competence but also on effective communication which is necessary to secure the co-operation of all those likely to be concerned.

CHAPTER 6

THE INTRODUCTION OF AUTOMATED ASSEMBLY: INVOLVEMENT OF PERSONNEL

INTRODUCTION

The successful introduction of automated assembly depends on the involvement and co-operation of a wide variety of personnel representing most of the company functions. In any progressive company wishing to develop automated assembly techniques all technical departments, from the drawing office to manufacturing supervisor, should be oriented towards the use of mechanical and automated assembly and considerable importance must be given to the training of staff and operators.

This chapter deals first with the company functions most likely to be involved in the evaluation and commissioning of a project to introduce automated assembly. After emphasising the need for effective communication throughout the project, it goes on to deal with those personnel who will be primarily involved with the new assembly machine once it has been accepted by production.

PERSONNEL INVOLVED IN THE EVALUATION AND COMMISSIONING OF THE PROJECT

When it has been established that a project to introduce some form of automated assembly is feasible, a Project Engineer is likely to be appointed and will take responsibility for the design, development and commissioning of an assembly machine. However, the successful introduction of automated assembly requires the involvement and active participation of a number of company functions. The main roles of the major departments likely to be involved in such a project are described below:

1. Product Design and Sales Staff

The enthusiasm and co-operation of designers and draughtsmen is an essential ingredient if a company is to make significant progress with the automation of assembly operations. Similarly, sales staff can contribute to the case for automated assembly by resisting customer requests for minor design variations. The company should therefore promote a positive policy for training the product designer and draughtsmen in the use of techniques which:

- reduce the number of parts in the assembly
- incorporate one-sided or "stack-up" assemblies*

---

*A "stack-up" assembly is an assembly or sub-assembly in which all components can be fitted together without turning it over or lifting it from its assembly jig or work pallet.

- set tolerances which can be maintained easily, bearing in mind the manufacturing methods to be used for each component
- educate sales staff in the need for reduction of unnecessary variety in product and packaging.

There should be at least one senior member of the firm who is capable of imparting these principles at either formal or informal design guide sessions. The drawing office and development staff must be constantly made aware of the necessity to adhere to the design principles listed above and they must also appreciate the quality problems inherent in the various processes used for the production of components.

2. Planning, Work Study and Standards

The company organisation must allow for close and informal co-operation between the design and the planning/work study staff from the beginning of the design of the product. In the smallest organisations it is likely that design and planning/work study will be done in the same office and possibly by the same people so there should be no problems of liaison. However, in medium-sized organisations lack of communication can often impede progress and it needs to be made clear by senior management that the drawing office and planning/work study need constant and free access to each other.

Work on the feasibility of introducing automated assembly is likely to commence in the planning section and their principal task is to ensure through work study (possibly using MTM-based techniques) that accurate times are established for any manual operations which may be required.

If a bonus or other payment by results system is in use it is very important that, where assembly machine operators are needed, the amount of work each has to do keeps them sufficiently occupied to work at at the rating generally prevailing in the rest of the factory. The same rule will apply when the workforce is paid by a flat-rate system. Even where the assembly machine is totally automated the attendant should be found sufficient work by combination with other suitable jobs in order to avoid unacceptably wide variations in workload for equal payment.

Finally, all sections and departments can benefit greatly from the presentation of all types of data in a standard form. Standards section should develop standard formats for work study data, layouts, costings etc., in consultation with the departments concerned.

3. Personnel Department

Well in advance of any detailed consideration of automated assembly the Personnel Department should have discussions with the workforce in order to obtain agreement on

- the determination of manning levels and, if possible, the use of work study to provide facts

- payment methods in those situations where it is not possible to compare the effort required in attending a machine with other jobs in the works
- equitable division of the savings in labour costs so that both the remaining labour and the company find it profitable to move to mechanised or automated assembly. This will apply principally where existing jobs are automated
- redeployment and, if necessary, redundancy agreements to cover operators displaced from existing jobs by automated assembly.

Where there is a Trades Union, negotiations can proceed in a conventional manner in accordance with agreed procedure. However, where there is no Trades Union, some form of consultative machinery needs to be set up. It must be emphasized that if the many pitfalls presented by the introduction of automated assembly are to be avoided, it is highly undesirable for a company to proceed without settling these matters first. The Personnel Department thus has a vital role to play in the introduction of automated assembly.

4. Manufacturing Management

Manufacturing management should become familiar with the nature of automated assembly well before introducing it into the firm. The Production Data Memoranda Series on Automated Assembly published by the Institution of Production Engineers provides valuable guidance and potential suppliers of assembly machines would probably help to provide the names of other companies who already use automated assembly. Visits to such companies and discussions with their management and line supervision would provide a great deal of practical information about the type of problems likely to be encountered.

In the larger firms some form of automated assembly will probably have been introduced already. However, the aims of the product designer, the assembly machine designer, the planning department and others need to be communicated clearly to the manufacturing management. Close liaison with the Personnel Department is also required in agreeing manning levels, redeployment agreements and payment methods as well as in determining guidelines for the selection of operators.

When automated assembly is about to be introduced it is essential that first line supervision should obtain a good technical appreciation of the equipment. Therefore, training schemes should be mounted which provide appreciation courses for Management and Supervision even if only to give them a genuine understanding of the possible causes of breakdowns and the time taken to rectify them.

The use of automated assembly methods highlights the need for Management to be safety-conscious because there may be a tendency for operators and maintenance technicians to try to beat the safety guarding in order to clear minor faults. The correct demarcation between the tasks the operator can undertake in clearing faults and the tasks that must be left for maintenance has to be clearly defined before the assembly machine goes into full production. It should be possible for Supervision to carry out minor adjustments and setting unless the works is so large that setters are specially employed for the job.

Manufacturing management should also ensure that simple diagrammatic instructions for operating the machine and for troubleshooting in the case of breakdowns are provided to the operator and the Maintenance Technician. The preparation of these sheets would be undertaken by Planning and the machine designer.

A stable workforce in the production unit operating automated assembly machines is highly desirable as a high turnover can cause a significant lowering of the assembly machine output rate. It should also be stressed that it may take six months or a year before an automatic assembly machine attains its design output. It is therefore important that Manufacturing and Personnel Management should adopt policies which contribute to job stability.

5. Quality Control

In the very smallest organisation Quality Control will probably be undertaken by the product designer. However, by the time the number of operators reaches 50 Quality Control is likely to be a full time job. Quality Control should be divorced from line management as far as reporting-responsibility is concerned whether or not automated assembly is used, but the introduction of automated assembly highlights the importance of quality control as an independent function.

Automated assembly machines will not generally accept the sort of faulty parts which can be accommodated easily by a manual assembler. Throughout the project to introduce an assembly machine the Quality Controller must remain in close contact with all those involved to ensure that they have a thorough appreciation of the quality requirements of both the components and the assembly.

The smaller companies would be well advised to make sure that their quality control personnel are capable of controlling quality at the levels demanded by automated assembly before embarking upon this technique. In most companies, however, the Quality Control Section has the advantage of being in possession of a wide range of technical knowledge which puts it in a unique position for problem solving. It is therefore frequently desirable that Quality Control should have a troubleshooting role during the commissioning of an assembly machine. This role involves finding and implementing satisfactory solutions to the manufacturing problems which will arise during the commissioning stage. These solutions may involve changing the design or dimensional tolerances of components, improving the method of manufacture of the components or making modifications to the assembly machine.

ENSURING COMMUNICATION DURING THE PROJECT

Controlling an automated assembly project can be difficult and even in organisations accustomed to using Project Engineers it is prudent to establish a co-ordinating committee to ensure that all concerned know what is happening. The Committee should ideally include the Project Engineer and representatives from Planning, Manufacturing Management, Product Design, Work Study, Quality Control, Machine Design, Cost Accounts and Personnel. There may be only two or three meetings of the full Committee during the course of the project but there should be frequent meetings of some of the sub-groups. Simple hand-written notes should be taken at all meetings, allowing a margin at the side of the notes so that responsibility for action can be indicated with initials and these notes can then be photocopied and circulated.

The Project Engineer will be concerned with liaison with the machine manufacturer and will have to spend a great deal of time following through the progress of the machine design and its construction. He will have to draw into his discussions with the machine maker those members of the co-ordinating committee whose work appertains at the appropriate time.

For many companies except the smallest it often pays to set up their own automated assembly machine-building facility. Where the company is in a particularly specialised field such a facility can be well worthwhile. It also helps in the preparation of specifications for more complicated machines which have to be purchased.

During the period when trials are taking place co-operation between departments is essential as the machine cannot be put into production until both Manufacturing Management and Quality Control are satisfied with performance. Trials should include a few long runs to demonstrate that the original aims have been sufficiently well met to justify putting the machine into production.

PERSONNEL INVOLVED AFTER COMMISSIONING

The introduction of automated assembly can frequently result in far-reaching changes in the jobs of operating personnel and maintenance.

1. Machine Operators

Even if an assembly shop were fully automated there would still be a need for some operators. Where low level automation or mechanised assembly is concerned operators will still be carrying out jobs similar to those done in manual assembly but the stress involved in machine operation can be higher and the consequences of carelessness can be expensive. The selection of good operators is therefore important.

It is generally advisable to select mature operators who have been employees for some time, have settled into the ways of the company and are level-headed and think about their work. The thought that the assembly machine is the operators' own should be promoted and encouraged. They should keep it clean and attend to minor adjustments which should be agreed to ensure the correct demarcation with the maintenance section.

A good manual assembler will not necessarily make a good automated assembly machine attendant and some people may become nervous if they have to act at regular intervals on a short timescale. As a result the variation in output which can be obtained from an automated assembly machine using different operators can be quite high. If possible, it is desirable to experiment in order to determine which operators get the best out of the machine. Generally some form of payment by results scheme will ensure consistent productivity but it requires very careful work study to see that equal effort in the various parts of the factory results in equal payment. If it is likely to be difficult to achieve such equity it would be preferable to establish a flat rate.

The training of operators is a vital aspect of introducing automated assembly and must be given careful attention. This means that even on the most simple machine at least half a day is required and where techniques are introduced which are totally new on the shop floor the training period may last a week or more.

The person who undertakes this important training will generally vary depending on the size of the company. Usually foremen and supervisors cannot devote the necessary time to training and the best way is for it to be done by a training specialist. This may not be possible in a small company or where there are only 1 or 2 assembly machines but where there are more than a dozen such machines, an experienced training officer will certainly justify his costs in terms of reduced downtime.

It has already been said that it is important to provide adequate training and that the learning curve will be longer than for manual assembly jobs. As a general rule it can be stated that the more the job moves away from manual assembly the more personal is the operators' involvement with the machinery.

2.   Maintenance Technicians

Maintenance Technicians for automated assembly machines need to be fully versed in all aspects of the work and they should ideally have had appropriate electrical, pneumatic, hydraulic and mechanical training. If at all possible the Technician should be involved in the manufacture of the assembly machine and thus develop a sound knowledge of the machine and all the associated control devices. This experience should be supplemented by further courses on aspects of automated assembly run by local colleges and by suppliers. Microprocessors will play an increasingly important part in the control function of assembly machines and the Maintenance Technician should become familiar with their applications.

The training programme for a Maintenance Technician should include some time spent on machine construction and testing. This on-the-job training should ideally be supplemented by courses in pneumatics, electronic controls and safety; suitable courses in these subjects are likely to be provided at the local Technical College or College of Further Education.

Although the all-purpose Maintenance Technician is the ideal solution to the problems of effective preventive and breakdown maintenance, the company may well have an agreement with the Trades Unions in relation to the demarcation of work between electricians and fitters. In this situation the fitter-technician and the electrical technician have to work as a team. There is no problem here providing that the situation is explained to the Trades Unions and that any resulting negotiations are settled before allocating duties to the technicians concerned.

Where the assembly machine is the first or only machine likely to be used, the recruitment of a suitable Maintenance Technician is crucial and the best course of action is to employ a person with electrical and pneumatic training. In the smaller companies (say 20 people) the Maintenance Technician would have to carry out other kinds of maintenance in addition to his work on the assembly machine in order to justify his full-time employment.

3. Line Supervision

Well before the machine is brought on to the shop floor, Supervision will have received basic training about the machine's intended performance and the principles on which it operates.

The pre-production run-up stage is an excellent training period for Supervision and also provides the opportunity to ensure that all operating procedures are understood and agreed and official instruction sheets for the machine are issued before the machine is eventually handed over to Production. Line Supervision will have the responsibility to see that these minor but important points are not overlooked as Project Engineers may be inclined to forget the sort of details which can make or break Supervision's attitudes to the new machine. A suitable Training Programme for Supervision would include an explanation of the economic and other reasons for introducing automated assembly, descriptions of Work Study details, manning levels and predicted output figures, and the associated Union Agreement, a detailed explanation of all the machine's functions together with the specification of the duties of both the operator and the Maintenance Technician.

Supervision will also need to be aware of the ultimate aims for output and the standard times for the various operations. This will allow them to monitor the learning period which may be quite extensive when operators have to perform tasks like loading or adjusting the machine within the operating cycle. A procedure for reporting daily output faults and downtime should be established and a suitable statement filled in by Supervision. By logging details in this manner valuable data can be fed back to Planning, the Project Engineer and the Machine Designer, and is invaluable for the subsequent design of assembly machines.

In view of the possible duration of breakdowns, Supervision should make arrangements for operators to do alternative work during these periods and a routine for achieving this may have to be developed to a greater extent than would be necessary with manual assembly methods.

Finally and most importantly, Supervision will have to ensure that correct operator working methods are maintained, especially when new operators are assigned to this work.

CHAPTER 7

ECONOMIC CONSIDERATIONS FOR AUTOMATED ASSEMBLY

*This chapter offers guidance on the general principles of capital
expenditure appraisal and as such is not written specifically
for expenditure on automated assembly machine tools.*

1. INTRODUCTION

Along with other proposals involving capital expenditure, a proposal for
automated assembly will have to go through a company's normal screening
process to see if it is financially acceptable or not. Capital expenditures are those
where the full financial benefit of the outlay is not normally realized within the
current financial year, but over a number of years in the future. The screening
process applied by an individual company may be more or less rigorous: simple
financial criteria only may be applied on a project by project basis; properly
programmed capital budgets may be evolved; information concerning revenue
and expenditure may be treated as being known with certainty or allowance
made in a variety of ways for the effects of uncertainty. In the limited scope of
this chapter the subject can only be treated at a relatively basic level, but the
references at the end of the chapter will enable the reader to pursue the subject
further if required.

Not all capital expenditure proposals in a company will generate directly
identifiable net profit or net positive cash flow, for example provision of canteens,
welfare facilities. As many of these services are taken for granted by employees
they may not generate any benefit to a company at all; indirectly though, a
company would suffer financially without them. Much of this kind of expenditure
has therefore to be carried by the other income generating activities of a firm, a
fact to be recognised when financial criteria are established for capital projects in
the latter areas. These criteria may seem high unless it is clearly understood that
they are allowing for expenditure of the kind just described and risk and
uncertainty.

2. INFORMATION REQUIREMENTS FOR CAPITAL EXPENDITURE PROPOSALS

In general the following information will be needed:

(a) Initial Capital Cost. This will have to include much more than the invoice
     cost of the equipment in question e.g. it may include costs for preparing a
     site for the equipment, for providing equipment to bring supplies to the

machine, take finished products away etc. Depending on the nature of the project the initial equipment capital cost could easily be doubled by these ancillary items.

(b) Working capital requirements. Working capital is likely to be necessary particularly where the project is either a new one or an expansion of an existing activity.

(c) Forecasts of revenue and operating expenses over the working life of an asset.

(d) Statements of the financial outcome of comparisons with alternative processes (where applicable).

(e) Evaluation of the financial returns of the proposal from items (a) to (d) above in comparison with company criteria on financial expenditure.

It will be noted that estimation and forecasting is heavily involved in obtaining this information. Forecasts are notoriously inaccurate hence the need to provide a means to test the effects uncertainty, see section (6).

3. GENERAL COST BENEFIT EXPECTATIONS OF AUTOMATED ASSEMBLY

Without attempting an exhaustive listing of items which could come under this heading, some of the more important benefits and costs which may be identified are:

(a) *Benefits:*
    Savings on direct labour
    Increases in output
    Greater repeatability of parts, hence fewer rejects and less inspection

(b) *Costs:*
    Initial capital outlay
    Increases in the number of indirect operators required for servicing
    Higher quality of engineer to service the line
    Increase in power consumption
    Floor space

It is recognised that Automated Assembly can be attained at different levels of sophistication in manufacture; the above represents some of the variables which will be common to most situations and which will have to be built into the expenditure proposals.

4. EVALUATING CAPITAL EXPENDITURE—METHODS

It is important to recognise that methods of evaluation may significantly influence the choice of projects. The apparent value to a firm of one project vis-a-vis another may change according to whether one method of appraisal is adopted against another. This is a common problem in accounting and does not imply any financial sleight of hand. Each of the alternative methods is based implicitly on a different philosophy of evaluation: management has to decide what approach it considers most appropriate to take. Nonetheless, it must be borne in mind

(a) that certain methods may restrict or even distort a capital expenditure programme.

(b) that they do not all neatly fit in ultimately with the usual criterion for assessing a firm's overall economic performance: the rate of return on capital employed. This means that it is not easy to assess whether or not appraisals have gone according to plan; their effect in the Profit and Loss account will not necessarily come through at the same point in time as may be expected from the appraisals themselves. For example appraisal methods based on cash flow analysis will give a different picture to ones based on normal accounting methods.

A desirable approach may seem to be to choose a method of evaluation which is consistent in its selection of the best projects for the firm over the long run: unfortunately reality is not so simple as this and many factors stand in the way of achieving such a goal.

Research Committee Occasional Paper[10] lists a number of the alternative methods which are used by firms. Here it is intended to concentrate only on four of the most common ones, giving a brief explanation of each and commenting on their individual characteristics.

The four are:

(a) Pay-back Period

(b) Accounting Rate of Return

(c) Discounted Cash Flow:
    (i) Yield or Internal Rate of Return
    (ii) Net Present Value

(a) *Pay-back period:* time taken to recover the initial capital outlay. Example: Select between Project A and B

| | Project A | | Project B | |
Year	Capital Cost £	Net Returns £	Capital Cost £	Net Returns £
0.............	1,000		1,000	
1.............		500		300
2.............		700		500
3.............		600		1,000
4.............		400		1,000

Straight application of simple pay-back to these figures would lead to selection of project A, since it returns the initial capital outlay between years 1 and 2 compared to between years 2 and 3 for project B. This is so even though Project B produces greater total returns. It would apply if A and B were totally different projects competing for limited capital resources or alternative means of attempting to realise a single objective.

Pay-back is widely used (not always by itself) and is *not* a method of indicating relative profitability amongst capital projects; it takes no account of earnings beyond the pay-back point.

Its merit is often said to be that in an uncertain world it is a measure which reduces risk; companies in a weak credit position or operating in volatile markets must certainly consider the pay-back periods, even if decisions are not ultimately wholly based upon it.

On the other hand, it does tend to act against the introduction of more advanced technology where lead-times before equipment becomes fully operational may be much greater than with conventional equipment.

(b) *Accounting Rate of Return:* The basic formula for this measure is given as:

$$\frac{\text{Net Profit after Depreciation}}{\text{Capital Employed}} \times 100$$

Variations could include net profit quoted as before or after tax. Profit is normally averaged over the anticipated life of the project.

The main advantage of this method is its simplicity and the fact that it corresponds in principle to the commonly adopted overall assessment of a company's performance: rate of return on capital employed on the company's assets in total. However, it does not distinguish the time profile over which net profit is obtained. A typical profile for an income-generating asset may look like this:

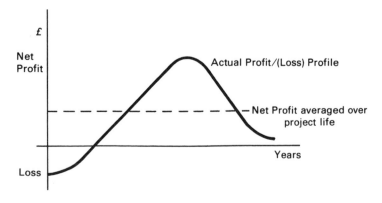

Fig 6

Recognition that averaging is a weakness in that money has a time value which goes unrecognised gives rise to the discounted cash flow approach described in the next section. The significance of calling it an "Accounting R.O.R" is that net profit is arrived at after charging depreciation and no allowance is made for the effect of time value of money as is the case in the discount cash flow method.

(c) *Discounted Cash Flow:* Cash flow is the identification of the points in time when cash either leaves or enters the firm (which is not the case for accruals accounting). These cash flows are then discounted to obtain their present values so that the series of cash outflows and cash inflows can be compared with each other on an equivalent basis.

Discounting is the process of compound interest in reverse. Thus if we have £100 to invest now and it could earn 10% p.a. interest, in one year's time we would expect to have £110. Putting the argument the other way round: if it was expected that £110 would be earned in one year's time, with a cost of capital (explained in section 5) of 10%, then it would have a present value of £100, discounted at 10%. For certain problems it may be desirable to work on a compound interest basis and evaluate cash flows at a terminal date, but the conventional method for simple project appraisal is to discount cash flows back to their present values. Recognition that money has a time value and that £1 earned now has not the same value as £1 earned next year or in ten year's time ensures that the varying cash flows of the typical industrial project are weighted to give each appropriate significance in the final evaluation.

Problems of dealing with the effects of inflation are not involved here; it is assumed that cash flows are stated as real values, i.e. values which are not being constantly depreciated as a result of inflation effects. Discounting may also be carried out on a discrete or continuous time period basis: the former is adopted here.

(i) *The Yield or Internal Rate of Return (I.R.R.) Method*
The object is to determine the exact discounted rate of return for a project, i.e. the rate which equates the present values of cash inflows and outflows.

Consider a simple example where it is assumed an automated assembly project produces the following incremental benefit and cost changes, i.e. the figures are the differences between an automated and say a manual assembly process.

Time Period (Years)	0	1	2	3	4
A. *Cash Inflow* (£): Direct Labour Saving.............		1000	1500	1500	1200
B. *Cash Outflow* (£): Capital Cost...........................	3048				
Increased Indirect.................. Cost of Operating..................		200	200	200	300
Net Cash Flow (A-B) (£)................	(3048)	800	1300	1300	900
Discount Factor (15%)...................	—	.870	.756	.658	.571
Discounted Net Cash Flow (£)........	(3048)	696	982.8	855.4	513.9
				3048	

(*N.B.*—Brackets used in Net Cash Flow line to distinguish cash out from cash in)

Discounted at 15% the two cash flows are exactly equal. This then is the Yield or I.R.R.—it states what the real return of the project is and it is implicit that the original capital outlay will also be recovered. In practice computer routines are available to determine this rate, avoiding a tedious manual search through printed tables (an example of a discount table is given at the end of the chapter). Modern hand calculators are frequently powerful enough to deal with these computations with minimal effort.

The figures are quoted at discrete intervals assumed to be a year, with 0 representing the present—whether such a broad approximation to the true timing of cash flows is sufficiently good has to be decided.

The figure of 15% must be compared with the firm's cost of capital to see if it is an acceptable return and ultimately, if it is, with other projects, where available capital is limited.

(ii) *Net Present Value Method (N.P.V.)*

Here the firm specifies the minimum acceptable discounted rate of return at which all projects are to be evaluated. The minimum rate will be close to the cost of capital to the firm—a negative discounted cash flow indicates a project which does not come up to a firm's requirements, whilst a positive one provides a margin beyond the minimum. Basically, projects with negative C.F. may be discarded unless some special circumstance prevails.

The N.P.V. is the absolute difference between the cash flows in and out. Thus, if 10% were assumed to be the minimum rate, the cash inflow of the preceeding example would be discounted to a total of £3,392: then,

£3,392 minus £3,048 (capital cost)
= + £344 = Net Present Value,
i.e. as is obvious in this case, this would be an acceptable project.

This is a simpler approach than identifying the Yield, but a ranking problem remains where the number of projects producing a positive N.P.V. would absorb more than the capital available for investment.

The Yield and N.P.V. methods do not always give results consistent with each other e.g. in the case of mutually exclusive projects (where acceptance of one project means rejection of another). For example a manufacturer may be considering one site against another for the purpose of building a new plant—he will select one or other site but not both: the alternatives are said to be mutually exclusive. The costs and revenue profiles of mutually exclusive projects are not necessarily by any means identical and in the simple situation it is generally safer to use the Net Present Value criterion rather than the Yield as the basis for selecting one of the alternatives.

Benefit Cost Ratios

Commonly expressed either as the ratio of the *net* discounted benefits of a project to the initial capital investment required or total discounted benefits to total costs.

A ratio of greater than one in both cases indicates an acceptable project, but the latter ratio is more useful in deciding between projects where capital is limited. This is because it shows the return generated by each pound of expenditure undertaken.

5. COST OF CAPITAL

Capital is not a free resource and in order to ensure capital expenditure is properly directed to securing a company's economic objectives, the cost of raising finance is the minimum criterion which revenue earning projects should aim to achieve.

The main sources of finance are:

(a) *External*
   (i) New Share Issues; Rights Issues
   (ii) Debenture and Loan Stocks
   (iii) Bank loans and overdrafts
(b) *Internal*
   (i) Depreciation provisions
   (ii) Ploughed-back profits

Internal sources (ploughed-back profit) provide the main source of funds for medium and longer term expenditures. They form, along with new share capital, part of the equity capital stream.

Calculating the cost of capital may be quite a subtle process, but a *basic* approach is to calculate a weighted average of the cost of each form of finance, weights being the proportions in which the finance is raised.

Type of Finance	Cost (%)	Proportion (%)
New Shares plus		
Depreciation plus Ploughed-back Profit.................	20	50
Medium Term Loan Capital..................................	14	30
Short-term Bank Loans......................................	10	20

The weighted average is 16.2%, which becomes the target for individual projects to realise as a minimum. The cost of the ordinary share capital takes into account the fact this is a company's risk capital and that risk varies from industry to industry. Medium and short-term loan capital bear less risk and consequently cost less. The ratio of share capital to fixed interest loan capital (the gearing ratio) must also be carefully considered by management in practice, especially as interest is an allowable charge before tax whereas dividends are not. With tax at 52%, the net interest cost to a company when the gross interest rate is say 10%, comes to 4.8%.

Taxation and Capital Allowances
The final impact on a firm's funds is the after-tax, after allowance cash flow. This is not normally calculated at the project manager level, but in the central accounting departments, because tax calculation must follow specific rules defined by the Inland Revenue.

The tax position as far as companies are concerned is that agreed profits are subject to corporation tax at 52% of agreed profits (on the imputation tax basis) and that capital expenditure is fully allowed against profits (assuming they are great enough) in the year in which that expenditure is incurred—so-called "free depreciation". Such expenditure is therefore treated about the same as wages or any other operating expense; it is a system intended to make investment expenditure as attractive as possible within the normal tax framework.

The question of allowances and incentives to invest provided by government beyond this basic tax allowance is a very complex one. Numerous schemes exist, but there is unfortunately no central reference point where they may all be examined together. Prominent amongst the schemes are those related to development areas where for example in South Wales, designated as a "Special" Development Area, it is possible to obtain grants of up to 22% for buildings and machinery and equipment. The grants are smaller in areas designated as "Development" and "Intermediate" areas. A Department of Industry Publication, "Incentives for Industry in the Areas for Expansion"; September, 1977, covers most of the incentives and allowances with respect to these areas.

Other sources of finance, grants and allowances may come from the National Enterprise Board and a wide variety of industrial sector and schemes such as that made available to the machine tool industry. These cover industry generally and not solely the development areas. In addition there are grants available from the European Community. Additional schemes such as those related to maintaining and creating employment (the Manpower Commission) must also be considered in their possible impact on running costs in a capital expenditure programme.

The after tax—after allowance calculations can make appreciable differences to alternative courses of action as compared to the pre tax etc. computations. Much will depend on the time profile of the various project cash flows.

6. ALLOWING FOR UNCERTAINTY

Capital expenditure proposals require estimates of revenue and cost to be made extending often for many years into the future. It is virtually impossible to make such estimates with absolute accuracy and therefore it is prudent to consider what might happen in the event of certain types and degrees of errors occurring. Sources of error are numerous and hardly need listing; a few obvious ones are changes in government policy, union reaction to new working methods and conditions, strength of overseas competition, unexpected product obsolescence and so on. Some methods for dealing with uncertainty are:

(a) *Simple sensitivity tests*

Select the factors which have a significant bearing on the economic success or otherwise of a project and see what the effect would be of failure to achieve the initial estimates for each factor in turn. This is really an elementary ad hoc approach, but does give some insight into project sensitivity.

For example, using the data of the yield method, what would the outcome look like if the initial estimates of direct labour saving were down by 15% each year in practice? The new direct labour saving values are:

	0	1	2	3	4
Saving (£).............................		850	1275	1275	1020

After deducting operating costs and discounting at 10%, the new total discounted savings are £2778, i.e. less than the initial capital outlay—the project would not break-even in such an event. After looking at all the important angles this way and taking into account the firm's financial strength and its attitude to risk taking, management may well not accept some projects which at first sight seem attractive; indeed, the comparative assessment of projects may change as well.

(b) *Risk Profiles*

Monte Carlo[6] simulation is used in an analysis which treats main factors as probabilistic variables.

In the first place, managers must be asked what weights (probabilities) they put on a range of possible outcomes for each factor. Thus the sales manager may be asked about the chances of being able to sell a product at different prices and the probable volume of sales at each price. For example:

Suggested Price/Unit Range	Weight (Probability) that this will be the actual price
1.0	.05
1.2	.15
1.4	.30
1.6	.35
1.8	.10
2.0	.05

With each factor assessed this way, a computer package may be used to select values at random from within each distribution and to produce a D.C.F. (Yield or N.P.V.) value for this particular combination of events. Repetition of this process say a few hundred times, which can be carried out very rapidly by the computer, typically produces a smooth profile as follows:

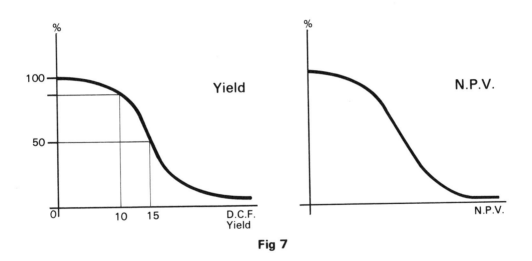

Fig 7

The Yield graph is interpreted as indicating there is at least a 50% chance of reaching a 15% yield and almost a 90% chance of obtaining 10%.

Objections are sometimes raised that it is not realistic to ask for the probability distributions of variables this way, but what is being requested is little more than a quantification of the "hunch" that might otherwise form the basis of the decision. Quantification however, permits a much clearer analysis of the situation to be made.

There is still the problem of the interrelationship between risk in one project and in another(s). The overall performance of the firm depends not just on the risks attached to a particular project, but on returns over time from other projects as well. It may well be found that management has to follow a policy of spreading risks through diversification; for example, certain high risk projects may be found worthwhile only if they result in high returns when other projects are yielding low returns.

In order to analyse capital expenditure problems of this nature, more advanced probabilistic models need to be developed, where net cash flow is treated as a random variable and its mean and variance calculated; criteria for the whole capital expenditure programme may be set such as maximising the expected return for a given level of risk. This topic goes well beyond the scope of the present text; references [1] [5] [6], provide further reading in the area.

7. MANAGEMENT'S ATTITUDE TO RISK TAKING

This has been mentioned earlier and is discussed briefly now to emphasise that calculated returns, supported or unsupported by an assessment of uncertainty, are not necessarily the last word in an investment decision. Firms and their managements differ in their ability and willingness to take risk. As a simple example, consider the following where a manager is offered the choice between two alternatives A and B; the details are:

Alternative A	*Alternative B*
.5 probability of a return of £1000	Certainty of £x
.5 probability of a return of £0	

The expected monetary value of alternative A, i.e. taking the probabilities into account is £500 (£1000 x .5 + £0 x .5). We wish to know the value £x, which, if offered as an alternative with complete certainty, would balance the outcomes and risks of A. The three possible outcomes are:

(a) £x is   £500, i.e. the manager likes to take a risk.

(b) £x is   £500, i.e. the manager is averse to taking risk.

(c) £x = £500 the only case where the manager's decision would correspond with expected returns without qualification.

It is thought probable that many managements tend toward being risk averse as in (b), may be for obvious reasons such as a weak financial position. However, the point is this attitude is imposed on top of calculations which may already apparently allow for risk and uncertainty. The degree of risk aversion is extremely difficult to measure; again, for further reading see references [1] [5] [6].

8. INFLATION[7]

Only the real return, i.e. after account has been taken of the effects of inflation, is of significance to a firm. High returns quoted on an historical basis are not only meaningless, but may well hide the downward slide to bankruptcy.

Allowing for inflation in capital expenditure proposals, so that expected real returns are always kept in sight, is not an easy task. Two main options exist:

(a) To work on the basis of current prices;

(b) To specifically allow for inflation in the calculations.

(a) Basically assumes inflationary cost increases can be matched by price increases such that the inflation on both sides cancels out. This is perhaps a hopeful approach, but in view of the difficulties of estimating inflation rates is probably widely accepted.

(b) Where inflation is brought directly into the calculations it may be through the use of:
    (i) A general index of inflation, like the Index of Retail Prices is often considered to be.
    (ii) Specific indices for different groups of expense and revenue.

Strictly (ii) is not really allowing for inflation, but the effect of price changes directly relevant only to the project(s) on hand. This would be an approach consistent with Current Cost Accounting[8].

Allowing for inflation and the effects of price changes is important where it is anticipated that the revenue and expense cash flows are likely to get out of phase with each other e.g. big increases in raw materials costs arising at a time of product market recession. Not only may real rates of return be reduced by inflation (a general tendency) but the effect on the firm's ability to finance the project must be questioned. However, in estimating the price change values, it must be realised that this another forecasting exercise which introduces its own errors.

9. CONCLUSION

Capital expenditure proposals of any magnitude should always be subjected to full testing from all points of view: alternative ways of achieving the objective; meeting required financial objectives; allowing for uncertainty and inflation. A firm's future propsperity depends in large measure on getting the answers right on investment proposals. Post-audit of actual outcomes against estimates is often neglected but is a vital source of information for future project planning.

Management of assets over their full life from initial design to disposal and the information required to do this, is a valuable approach expounded by the Life Cycle Costing system[9]. This is an area where co-operation between engineers and accountants in Capital Appraisal developments is most essential. There may well be a trade off between high initial capital outlays associated with low running costs as compared to say low initial outlay and relatively high running costs. The difference between the two circumstances is often related to reliability and maintenance of equipment and it is possible that a high degree of reliability together with relatively low maintenance can be built into equipment at the outset but result in higher capital costs. Conversely, an apparently equivalent but cheaper machine in terms of these capital requirements can subsequently result in high maintenance costs. Without good engineering information this situation can not be properly analysed and the tendency will be towards acceptance of the equipment which carries the lower initial outlay. Establishment of the Life Cycle Costing system will help both engineers and accountants to realise more fully the nature of the alternatives they are dealing with.

This chapter can only be regarded as introductory to an extensive subject area.

READING LIST
1. Investment Appraisal: Evaluating Risk and Uncertainty. *I.C.M.A.*
2. Corporate Planning. *I.C.M.A.*
3. Capital Budgeting and Company Finance. *Merrett and Sykes, Longmans.*
4. The Finance and Analysis of Capital Projects. *Merrett and Sykes, Longmans.*
5. The Economics of Capital Budgeting. *Bromwich, Penguin.*
6. Management of Company Finance. *Samuels and Wilkes, Nelson.*
7. Management Accounting in Inflationary Conditions. *Cox and Hewgill, I.C.M.A.*
8. Inflation Accounting Steering Group: Exposure Draft 18. *Morpeth Committee.*
9. Life Cycle Costing in the Management of Assets: A Guide. *Department of Industry.*
10. Research Committee Occasional Paper Number 7 "Investment Appraisal and Inflation". *Institute of Chartered Accountants.*

DISCOUNT TABLES

TABLE A—PRESENT VALUE OF ONE UNIT OF CURRENCY

Years Hence	1%	2%	4%	6%	8%	10%	12%	14%	15%	16%	18%	20%	22%	24%	25%	26%	28%	30%	35%	40%	45%	50%
1	0.990	0.980	0.962	0.943	0.926	0.909	0.893	0.877	0.870	0.862	0.847	0.833	0.820	0.806	0.800	0.794	0.781	0.769	0.741	0.714	0.690	0.667
2	0.980	0.961	0.925	0.890	0.857	0.826	0.797	0.769	0.756	0.743	0.718	0.694	0.672	0.650	0.640	0.630	0.610	0.592	0.549	0.510	0.476	0.444
3	0.971	0.942	0.889	0.840	0.794	0.751	0.712	0.675	0.658	0.641	0.609	0.579	0.551	0.524	0.512	0.500	0.477	0.455	0.406	0.364	0.328	0.296
4	0.961	0.924	0.855	0.792	0.735	0.683	0.636	0.592	0.572	0.552	0.516	0.482	0.451	0.423	0.410	0.397	0.373	0.350	0.301	0.260	0.226	0.198
5	0.951	0.906	0.822	0.747	0.681	0.621	0.567	0.519	0.497	0.476	0.437	0.402	0.370	0.341	0.328	0.315	0.291	0.269	0.223	0.186	0.156	0.132
6	0.942	0.888	0.790	0.705	0.630	0.564	0.507	0.456	0.432	0.410	0.370	0.335	0.303	0.275	0.262	0.250	0.227	0.207	0.165	0.133	0.108	0.088
7	0.933	0.871	0.760	0.665	0.583	0.513	0.452	0.400	0.376	0.354	0.314	0.279	0.249	0.222	0.210	0.198	0.178	0.159	0.122	0.095	0.074	0.059
8	0.923	0.853	0.731	0.627	0.540	0.467	0.404	0.351	0.327	0.305	0.266	0.233	0.204	0.179	0.168	0.157	0.139	0.123	0.091	0.068	0.051	0.039
9	0.914	0.837	0.703	0.592	0.500	0.424	0.361	0.308	0.284	0.263	0.225	0.194	0.167	0.144	0.134	0.125	0.108	0.094	0.067	0.048	0.035	0.026
10	0.905	0.820	0.676	0.558	0.463	0.386	0.322	0.270	0.247	0.227	0.191	0.162	0.137	0.116	0.107	0.099	0.085	0.073	0.050	0.035	0.024	0.017
11	0.896	0.804	0.650	0.527	0.429	0.350	0.287	0.237	0.215	0.195	0.162	0.135	0.112	0.094	0.086	0.079	0.066	0.056	0.037	0.025	0.017	0.012
12	0.887	0.788	0.625	0.497	0.397	0.319	0.257	0.208	0.187	0.168	0.137	0.112	0.092	0.076	0.069	0.062	0.052	0.043	0.027	0.018	0.012	0.008
13	0.879	0.773	0.601	0.469	0.368	0.290	0.229	0.182	0.163	0.145	0.116	0.093	0.075	0.061	0.055	0.050	0.040	0.033	0.020	0.013	0.008	0.005
14	0.870	0.758	0.577	0.442	0.340	0.263	0.205	0.160	0.141	0.125	0.099	0.078	0.062	0.049	0.044	0.039	0.032	0.025	0.015	0.009	0.006	0.003
15	0.861	0.743	0.555	0.417	0.315	0.239	0.183	0.140	0.123	0.108	0.084	0.065	0.051	0.040	0.035	0.031	0.025	0.020	0.011	0.006	0.004	0.002
16	0.853	0.728	0.534	0.394	0.292	0.218	0.163	0.123	0.107	0.093	0.071	0.054	0.042	0.032	0.028	0.025	0.019	0.015	0.008	0.005	0.003	0.002
17	0.844	0.714	0.513	0.371	0.270	0.198	0.146	0.108	0.093	0.080	0.060	0.045	0.034	0.026	0.023	0.020	0.015	0.012	0.006	0.003	0.002	0.001
18	0.836	0.700	0.494	0.350	0.250	0.180	0.130	0.095	0.081	0.069	0.051	0.038	0.028	0.021	0.018	0.016	0.012	0.009	0.005	0.002	0.001	0.001
19	0.828	0.686	0.475	0.331	0.232	0.164	0.116	0.083	0.070	0.060	0.043	0.031	0.023	0.017	0.014	0.012	0.009	0.007	0.003	0.002	0.001	
20	0.820	0.673	0.456	0.312	0.215	0.149	0.104	0.073	0.061	0.051	0.037	0.026	0.019	0.014	0.012	0.010	0.007	0.005	0.002	0.001	0.001	
21	0.811	0.660	0.439	0.294	0.199	0.135	0.093	0.064	0.053	0.044	0.031	0.022	0.015	0.011	0.009	0.008	0.006	0.004	0.002	0.001		
22	0.803	0.647	0.422	0.278	0.184	0.123	0.083	0.056	0.046	0.038	0.026	0.018	0.013	0.009	0.007	0.006	0.004	0.003	0.001	0.001		
23	0.795	0.634	0.406	0.262	0.170	0.112	0.074	0.049	0.040	0.033	0.022	0.015	0.010	0.007	0.006	0.005	0.003	0.002	0.001			
24	0.788	0.622	0.390	0.247	0.158	0.102	0.066	0.043	0.035	0.028	0.019	0.013	0.008	0.006	0.005	0.004	0.003	0.002	0.001			
25	0.780	0.610	0.375	0.233	0.146	0.092	0.059	0.038	0.030	0.024	0.016	0.010	0.007	0.005	0.004	0.003	0.002	0.001	0.001			
26	0.772	0.598	0.361	0.220	0.135	0.084	0.053	0.033	0.026	0.021	0.014	0.009	0.006	0.004	0.003	0.002	0.002	0.001				
27	0.764	0.586	0.347	0.207	0.125	0.076	0.047	0.029	0.023	0.018	0.011	0.007	0.005	0.003	0.002	0.002	0.001	0.001				
28	0.757	0.574	0.333	0.196	0.116	0.069	0.042	0.026	0.020	0.016	0.010	0.006	0.004	0.002	0.002	0.002	0.001	0.001				
29	0.749	0.563	0.321	0.185	0.107	0.063	0.037	0.022	0.017	0.014	0.008	0.005	0.003	0.002	0.002	0.001	0.001	0.001				
30	0.742	0.552	0.308	0.174	0.099	0.057	0.033	0.020	0.015	0.012	0.007	0.004	0.003	0.002	0.001	0.001	0.001					
40	0.672	0.453	0.208	0.097	0.046	0.022	0.011	0.005	0.004	0.003	0.001	0.001										
50	0.608	0.372	0.141	0.054	0.021	0.009	0.003	0.001	0.001	0.001												

Reproduced from Management Accounting in Inflationary Conditions. I.C.M.A.

APPENDIX 1

A selection of currently used examples of feeding devices, orientating mechanisms, escapements and transfer mechanisms extracted from the series of twenty volumes on automated assembling techniques published by and available from the Institution of Production Engineers under the following section headings:

Section 1 Hopper Feeders.

Section 2 Orientating Mechanisms & Escapements.
Published in 4 Parts.

Section 3 Component Placement Mechanisms.
Published in 4 Parts.

Section 4 Workhead Mechanisms.
Published in 6 Parts.

Section 5 Transfer Mechanisms.
Published in 4 Parts.

Section 6 Control Systems.

INSTITUTION OF PRODUCTION ENGINEERS

FEEDING DEVICES FOR AUTOMATED ASSEMBLING

CENTREBOARD HOPPER FEEDER

Suitability

Spheres, plain or headed pins, screws, bolts and U-shaped components can be handled satisfactorily by this hopper feeder.

General Description

The centreboard is a blade arranged to oscillate or reciprocate vertically within a fixed hopper, which usually has its base sloping towards the centreboard. Oscillating centreboards are pivoted at a point below the feed chute.

The top of the centreboard is shaped, usually by grooving, to correspond with part of the profile of the components. It is arranged to be flush with or slightly below the bottom of the hopper when in the stroke down position and its top edge should then be substantially horizontal, and in the stroke up position must attain a slope of sufficient angle to cause the components to roll or slide towards the feed tube or chute, and must be high enough to clear the bulk in the hopper.

Increased rates of feed can be obtained by using multiple centreboards in one hopper and mounted on a common shaft.

Bulk Separating Action

As the centreboard passes upwards through the bulk, it tends to raise a number of components which are retained by the shape of its top edge. Components not sufficiently orientated to the centreboard and any remaining on it at the commencement of the downstroke are returned to the bulk.

The number of components separated per cycle depends upon:-

      (1) components size in relation to length of centreboard

      (2) stability of components when moving towards feed chute

      (3) number of centreboards

Orientating Action

The orientating action is positive with many of the shapes which can be handled but some may have to be supplemented by a secondary device.

The action which takes place is provided by the shape of the top edge of the centreboard, the sliding or rolling action, and the gate formed by the entrance to the feed tube or chute.

Hopper

The hopper is a fixed container open at the top and provided with a slot through which the centreboard passes. The slot must be a close fit if small components are to be handled and may be provided with a downward extension to enclose the centreboard if a liquid-tight hopper is required.

_P_D**680008**

The sides of the hopper may be made vertical to give maximum storage space, the floor on each side should slope towards the centreboard to prevent dead areas from which components would not feed.   When multiple centreboards are used the floor between the slots should be in the form of an inverted V; if the distance between the centreboards is too close for this to be practicable, these areas would be made to slope towards one of the centreboards.

Significant Features

Several components tend to be separated from the bulk at each cycle, but due to their single-file formation the number discharged per cycle is limited by the time available for them to pass into the feed tube.   It is therefore preferable that the centreboard is given a dwell period in the stroke-up position.

To prevent jamming and consequent damage to components, the bottom edge of the centreboard must not be allowed to rise above the slot in the hopper floor, and either the front wall of the hopper or a guide must be curved to fit close to the radius of the front edge of the centreboard.   The centreboard pivot should be located outside the hopper, refer to illustration.

If the hopper and centreboard are properly proportioned the whole of the bulk can be discharged.

This hopper feeder is quiet in operation.

It is sometimes necessary to provide an auxiliary device at position 'A' (see sketch) to clear mis-orientated components from the entry to the gate.   This can be in the form of a reciprocating slide, a wheel, a brush, or an air blast.

Typical Equipment Dimensions and Speeds

Centreboard length   — 380 mm.

Centreboard thickness   — 12 mm. (dependent upon components size)

Hopper width for single centreboard — 150 mm.

Centreboard speed   — 15 cycles per minute

Typical Component Dimensions and Rates of Feed

(i) 6 mm. diameter × 50 mm. long dowel pins fed at 80 per minute with centreboard having grooved top edge.

(ii) 12 mm. diameter cocktail cherries in syrup fed at 150 per minute with centreboard having grooved top edge.

(iii) No. 8 woodscrews × 38 mm. long fed at 300 per minute with six centreboards having slotted top edge.

Tendency to Damage Components

As bulk is stationary and return drop of rejected components is low, this feeder causes little damage to components if designed correctly (see Hopper and Significant Features).

Drive

Electric motor with reduction gear driving eccentric or cam with suitable linkage to centreboard, or alternatively by air cylinder.

CENTREBOARD HOPPER FEEDER

level of components

Groove for component

Part section on 'X'-'X'

'X'

CENTREBOARD
BLADE

Position 'A'

Components level in
hopper

HOPPER

GUIDE

'X'

FEED CHUTE

issue 1

INSTITUTION OF PRODUCTION ENGINEERS

FEEDING DEVICES FOR AUTOMATED ASSEMBLING

VIBRATORY BOWL HOPPER FEEDER

Suitability

These hopper feeders can handle a wide variety of components. Their use is not confined to any particular shape, and relatively fragile parts can be handled without damage.

General Description

Components are loaded in bulk into the bowl-shaped hopper, which is usually supported by a number of inclined leaf springs, the ends of which are securely attached to the bowl and to a heavy base. A vibrator unit is also connected between the hopper and the base so that the hopper is caused to reciprocate in a vertical plane whilst oscillating in a horizontal plane.

The combination of these two movements causes the components to move outwards towards the side wall of the hopper and to climb a spiral flight attached around the inner periphery of the hopper. On reaching the top of the flight, the components cross the side wall of the hopper for delivery into a feed chute.

Bulk Separating Action

The bottom of the hopper is made slightly convex or conical to assist the outward movement of the components as they slowly rotate around the hopper under the influence of the vibration. Components adjacent to the side wall on reaching the flight commence to climb it. Separation is achieved by making the flight just wide enough to support components in single file.

Orientating Action

Orientation of the component is usually achieved by incorporating a series of selector devices in the flight to test the attitudes of the components as they climb. Correctly orientated components pass through all the selectors; those incorrectly orientated are rejected back into the hopper.

Hopper

The hopper is in the form of an open-top circular bowl with a substantially vertical side wall, and a slightly convex or conical bottom.

It may be fabricated from sheet steel or cast in aluminium alloy, but the bottom must be of sufficient rigidity to avoid secondary vibrations. In the latter case the spiral flight can be cast integrally and operation is quieter as resonance is reduced, and the fatigue life can be improved. Fabricated steel is more economical for hoppers constructed on a one off basis.

Significant Features

The feed rate may be adjusted by

> (1) alteration of vibration amplitude, usually by varying the
> voltage with electro-magnetic vibrators

VIBRATORY BOWL HOPPER FEEDER

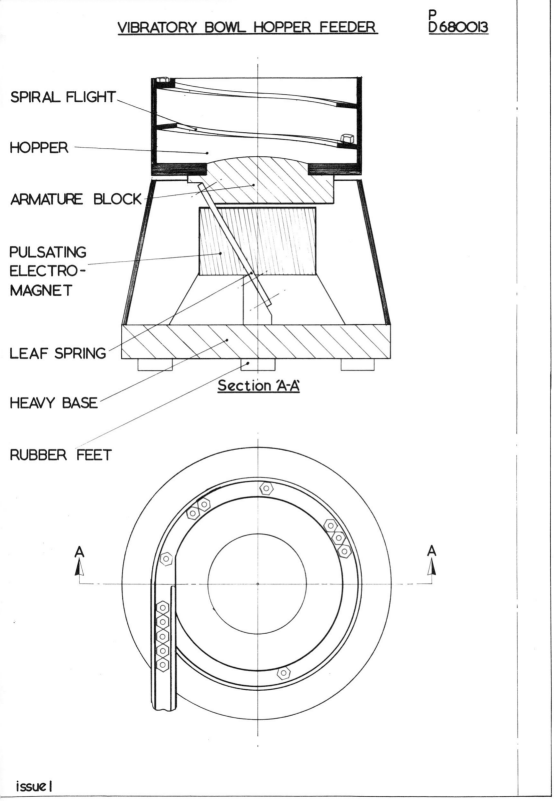

SPIRAL FLIGHT

HOPPER

ARMATURE BLOCK

PULSATING ELECTRO- MAGNET

LEAF SPRING

HEAVY BASE

RUBBER FEET

Section 'A-A'

A   A

issue I

(2) the use of multiple flights and feed chutes

(3) by stacking hoppers two-high, or more, on to one vibrator unit

(4) by bonding materials such as P.V.C. or rubber to the inner surfaces of the hopper and to the flight to increase the efficiency of the frictional driving force.

These hopper feeders tend to be sensitive to the weight of the bulk, which can give rise to erratic feeding. They are noisy in operation, but lining of hopper and flight as (4) above can reduce the noise emanating from component rattle.

Hoppers with detachable flights may be provided with interchangeable portions of the flight to permit quick changeover of selector devices for handling a range of components.

Complex orientation within the hopper can be successfully developed, taking advantage of the positive force acting on the components during their ascent of the flight.

Typical Equipment Dimensions and Speeds

Hopper bowl diameters from 75 mm. to 1000 mm. are known.

A typical speed of feed is 6 m. per minute with a 300 mm. diameter hopper.

Typical electrical characteristics for a 450 mm. diameter hopper with electro-magnetic vibrator are 220-240v 50 cycle a.c. input current 1.25 amps, power consumption 50 watts approximately.

Typical Component Dimensions and Rates of Feed

Nozzle bodies 40 mm. long; 2 diameters 18.5 mm. × 20 mm. long and 14 mm. × 20 mm. long. Fed at 40 per minute fully orientated.

Ceramic bead 23.8 mm. × 15.6 mm. × 4.7 mm. grooved along one side 6.2 mm. wide × 3.1 mm. deep. Fed at 60 per minute fully orientated.

Rubber grommet 15.6 mm. diameter × 9.5 mm. long. Fed at 150 per minute fully orientated, in 450 mm. diameter hopper.

Aluminium caps, 33 mm. diameter × 15.6 mm. long × .25 mm. thick. Fed at 500 per minute fully orientated in 450 mm. diameter hopper.

Tapered polythene spouts 37.5 mm. long with 15.6 mm. diameter flange at large end. Fed at 150 per minute fully orientated in 600 mm. diameter hopper.

Tendency to Damage Components

The gentle action of these hopper feeders causes little or no damage provided that excessive feed rates are avoided.

Drive

Electro-magnetic or pneumatic vibrator unit.

INSTITUTION OF PRODUCTION ENGINEERS

FEEDING DEVICES FOR AUTOMATED ASSEMBLING

RISING PIN HOPPER FEEDER

Suitability

These hopper feeders are suitable for most cup-shaped components, such as bottle caps and jar closures, and for many U-shaped components.

General Description

Components are loaded in bulk into a bowl-shaped hopper consisting of a fixed wall within which a disc rotates at constant speed about a vertical axis. A number of pins are carried in guides in the disc with their lower ends in contact with a fixed face cam. The pins rise to lift components clear of the bulk and feed them with their open ends downwards.

Bulk Separating Action

As the disc rotates, the pins are caused to rise into the bulk so that suitably orientated components are lifted clear and retained on the pins until they are located above a curved guide which is slotted centrally to clear the pins. The pins retract and deposit the separated components on to the guide. As the action is positive, preceding components are pushed along the guide into the feed chute.

The number of components separated per revolution of the bowl depends upon:-

(1) The number of pins; this is limited by the need for the circular pitch to be large enough to prevent components from bridging across two pins

(2) orientation of components within the bulk

(3) component shape

(4) stability: components which are not properly located on the pins fall back into the bulk.

Orientating Action

Where the proportions of a cup-shaped component enable domed top pins to be used, the separating action can provide positive orientation. Where the pins must have large diameter flat tops, components may become separated with the open end upwards, but if they have a flanged or curled edge, such wrongly orientated components may be rejected by a suitable gate at the mouth of the guide.

Hopper

The hopper is in the form of a circular vertical side wall with the floor formed by a rotating disc. The centre of the disc is of convex or conical form to assist in positioning the components over the pins as the hopper rotates.

The disc may be fabricated from steel, but is usually cast in iron or aluminium to provide integral guides for the pins.

PD**680015**

Significant Features

The rotation of the disc and the lifting of the pins causes a constant agitation which assist in orientating components to a suitable position for pick-up; therefore fairly constant feed rates may be achieved.

Care must be taken in the design to prevent components becoming jammed between pins and the hopper or guide.

Typical Equipment, Dimensions and Speeds

As the height of the bulk permissible in the hopper must be below the guide, the capacity of the hopper depends largely upon its diameter, which also governs the numbers of pins which may be used.

A typical example has a 460 mm. diameter hopper rotating at 20 r.p.m.

Typical Component Dimensions and Rates of Feed

Bayonet fitting and screwed caps for electric lamps fed at 300 per minute by above example.

Tendency to Damage Components

Provided that components are not vulnerable from the tumbling action, there is little risk of damage if the design is such that jams rarely occur.

Drive

By electric motor and reduction gear.

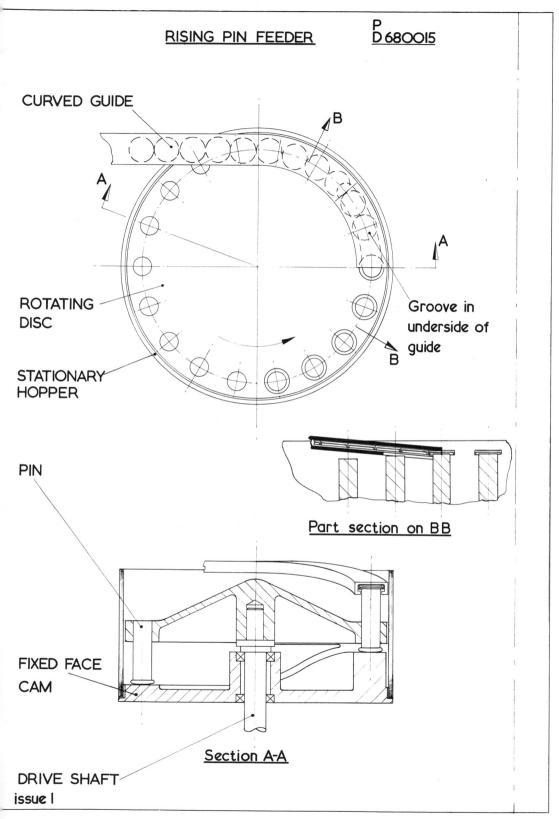

RISING PIN FEEDER

P
D 680015

CURVED GUIDE

B

A

A

ROTATING
DISC

Groove in
underside of
guide

B

STATIONARY
HOPPER

PIN

Part section on BB

FIXED FACE
CAM

Section A-A

DRIVE SHAFT
issue 1

INSTITUTION OF PRODUCTION ENGINEERS

ORIENTATING MECHANISMS AND ESCAPEMENTS

The mechanism illustrated on the drawing is an extremely useful and effective device for combining escapement and elevation of bar and tubular components.

Description of the Escapement Mechanism

Components are fed continuously along an inclined feed chute until their travel is arrested by the leading component coming into contact with the back face of an elevating block, (as shown on the left hand view of the drawing).

In this view, swinging pawls are shown positioned along the fixed side of the elevating chute. The same number of pawls are positioned in the side of the elevating block, these being set slightly below the level of the pawls in the fixed side.

The overall length of the component will determine whether each axis will require one or more pawls to support it stably.

Components are fed to the work area in the following sequence:

The extension of the pneumatic cylinder causes the elevating block to lift each component supported on the pawls and on the angular face of the elevating block. The length of stroke is adjusted so as to slightly exceed the pitch between the pawls.

As the components are elevated, the swinging pawls positioned in the fixed side of the elevating chute will be pushed aside but will swing back into their normal position as the components pass clear.

The components thus move progressively up the elevating chute at a single pitch per stroke. The leading component is directed, by the deflection of the leaf spring, into the exit chute leading to the work area.

When the pneumatic cylinder retracts, the components remain lodged on the pawls positioned in the fixed side of the elevating chute while the pawls positioned in the elevating block swing clear and then underneath a component in a position where they are ready to elevate the component on the subsequent actuation.

Although only two pairs of pawls are illustrated on the drawing, further sets may be added to achieve any desired elevation of the components.

The swinging pawls can be returned to their normal horizontal position either by gravity or by spring action. Support for the load resting on the pawls is obtained by contact between the heel of the pawl and the stop plate.

Dimensions of typical component: 20 mm outside diameter × 30 mm length.

Material: steel cylindrical shafts, but applicable to other materials and components of suitable configuration including stepped diameters.

Feed rate achieved with this component: 2400 per hour.

Typical component being fed :—

         Cylindrical shaft

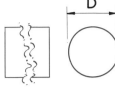

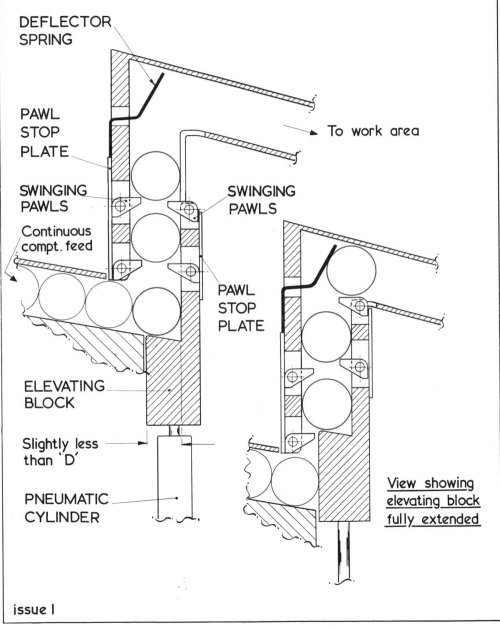

DEFLECTOR
SPRING

PAWL
STOP
PLATE

To work area

SWINGING
PAWLS

SWINGING
PAWLS

Continuous
compt. feed

PAWL
STOP
PLATE

ELEVATING
BLOCK

Slightly less
than 'D'

PNEUMATIC
CYLINDER

View showing
elevating block
fully extended

issue 1

INSTITUTION OF PRODUCTION ENGINEERS

ORIENTATING MECHANISMS AND ESCAPEMENTS

The illustration on the drawing depicts an escapement mechanism for feeding components possessing a circular or symmetrical section with a facility for a change of component direction or orientation. It may be used for simply changing the direction of feed and pushing the component towards a working area or for assembling a component to its mating counterpart.

Description of the Escapement Mechanism

Components are fed continuously through a feed chute of appropriate section and into a clearance hole of similar section formed in the main block.

An indexing shaft is positioned across the feed axis of the components and a hole of the same section is formed through the shaft in alignment with the hole in the main block. When the components are fed through the main block the leading component comes to rest with its body length enclosed within the diameter of the indexing shaft.

The diameter of the shaft should be slightly greater than the overall length of the component (shown as 'L' on the drawing) and the shaft may be undercut to approximately $0.9\,L$ diameter at the whole position to provide clearance between the following component and the indexing shaft during its rotation.

The indexing shaft can be rotated by progressive or reciprocating increments of 90° clockwise or anticlockwise according to the orientation desired. The component is thereby indexed into alignment with the exit hole and the actuation of the pusher bar is sequenced to this rotation.

Dimensions of typical component: 6 mm diameter × 18 mm length.

Material: steel dowel pins; but applicable to other materials and configurations.

Feed rate achieved with this component: 2400 per hour.

ORIENTATING MECHANISMS & ESCAPEMENTS P D 680318

Typical component being fed :—

Plain cylinders

L

Continuous feed of components

A

TO ACTUATOR

INDEXING SHAFT

L + clearance

0.9 x L

Section A-A

PUSHER BAR

Indexing shaft may have progressive or reciprocating rotation in increments of 90°

ASSEMBLY POSITION

View showing indexing shaft rotated through 90° and component ejected

INSTITUTION OF PRODUCTION ENGINEERS

TRANSFER MECHANISMS

This high speed cam-actuated transfer mechanism has been in constant service over a long period of time.

It is robustly constructed and transmits a rotary intermittent movement to the output drive shaft shown on page 1 of the drawing.

Description of the Transfer Mechanism

The main elements of this mechanism are shown on page 1, and page 2 contains diagrams which show its indexing sequence.

Referring to view (a) on page 2, it can be seen that two face cams are mounted on the horizontally aligned input drive shaft. Rotation of this shaft causes both cams to rotate.

The mechanism in its "start" position is shown on page 2 of the drawing at view (a). At this position, the rotary table, which is mounted on the vertically aligned output drive shaft, is stationary.

The cycling movement of the mechanism commences with disengagement of the non-return pawl caused by the cam/roller set-up as shown on the drawing at view (b) on page 2.

Continued rotation of the two cams causes the indexing pawl to rotate the divisor plate, through engagement in one of its notches, until the divisor plate reaches the position illustrated on page 2 at view (c).

As the cams continue to rotate, the non-return pawl re-engages in the divisor plate and the indexing pawl commences to return to its "start" position, as shown at view (d) on page 2 of the drawing.

Type of transfer :− Rotary − intermittent

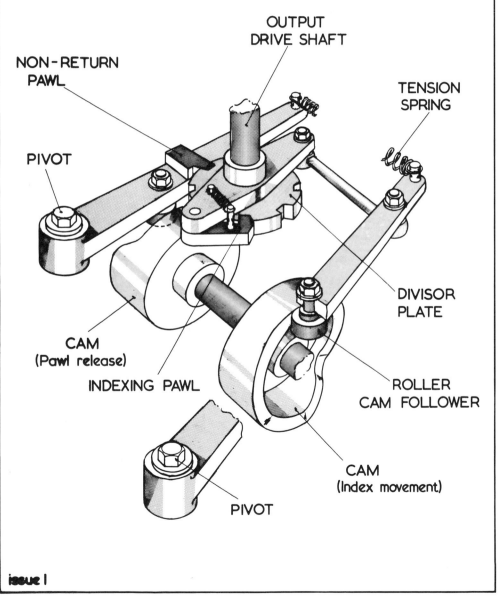

NON−RETURN
PAWL

OUTPUT
DRIVE SHAFT

TENSION
SPRING

PIVOT

CAM
(Pawl release)

INDEXING PAWL

DIVISOR
PLATE

ROLLER
CAM FOLLOWER

CAM
(Index movement)

PIVOT

issue 1

Type of transfer   :–   Rotary – intermittent

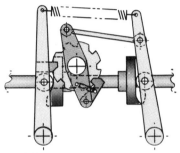

(a)Start position

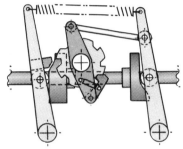

(b)Non-return pawl is disengaged

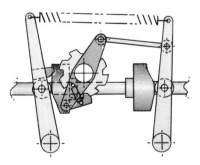

(c)Indexing pawl rotates divisor plate through one increment of index

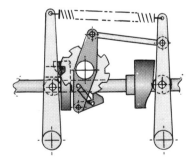

(d)Non-return pawl is engaged and indexing pawl returns to start position

Diagrams showing sequence of indexing

issue I

INSTITUTION OF PRODUCTION ENGINEERS

TRANSFER MECHANISMS

This design has been employed over a long period of time and is used on an in-line assembling machine for indexing assembly fixtures along a linear path.

Description of the Transfer Mechanism

The assembly fixtures are linked together, in the manner shown on the drawing, and in fact form an endless chain.

This chain of fixtures passes over a driving pulley, which is situated at the same end of the machine as the crosshead, and over a freewheeling pulley at the machine's opposite extremity.

Rotation of the input drive shaft causes the crosshead to travel along the slide bars into the position shown on the drawing.

As the crosshead moves towards this position, the two spring-loaded pawls rise over and then engage upon the index pins mounted horizontally in the assembly fixtures.

Continued rotation of the input drive shaft withdraws the crosshead towards the drive shaft whilst at the same time causing the assembly fixtures to travel through one increment of index along the guide track.

Upon finalisation of this withdrawal movement, a shot bolt locates one of the assembly fixtures and the workhead performs its assembling function.

When the workhead has completed its task, the shot bolt is withdrawn clear of the fixture and in the assembling time the crosshead is moving forward again to latch the pawls over another set of index pins.

In the example seen, the eccentric webs, shown on the drawing, were utilised to actuate the vertically reciprocating movement of the workhead, thus ensuring synchronisation of the workhead to the crosshead travel.

This particular mechanism moved the assembly fixtures through one increment of index in one second.

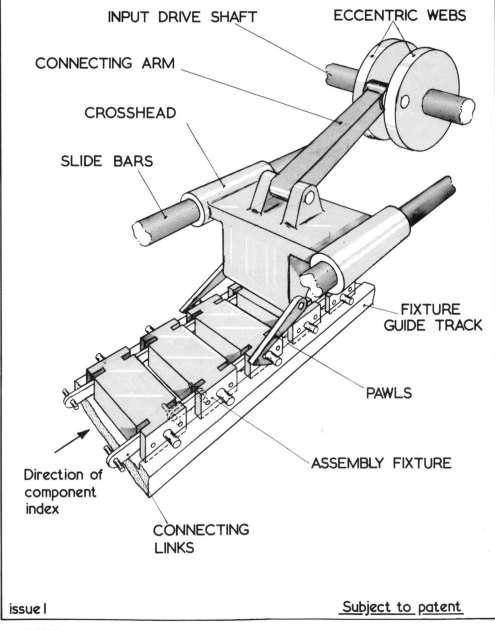

TRANSFER MECHANISMS

Type of transfer   :—   Linear — intermittent

INPUT DRIVE SHAFT

ECCENTRIC WEBS

CONNECTING ARM

CROSSHEAD

SLIDE BARS

FIXTURE
GUIDE TRACK

PAWLS

ASSEMBLY FIXTURE

Direction of
component
index

CONNECTING
LINKS

issue 1

Subject to patent

SEVENTY FOUR

APPENDIX 2

DIRECTORY

MANUFACTURERS AND SUPPLIERS OF AUTOMATED ASSEMBLY EQUIPMENT

Albe (England) Ltd.
Newton Works, 51 Bideford Avenue, Perivale,
Greenford, Middlesex
Telephone 01-997 7282   *Telex* 935178

Aylesbury Automation Ltd.
Mandeville Road, Aylesbury, Buckinghamshire
Telephone Aylesbury 5911   *Telex* 83210

Badalex Ltd.
Weybridge Trading Estate, Weybridge,
Surrey KT15 2RH
Telephone Weybridge 48311   *Telex* 27695

Brandone Machine Tool Ltd.
48 Station Road, Harrow, Middlesex HA1 2SQ
Telephone 01-863 7141   *Telex* 922668

Brown and Ward Ltd.
(sole agents for Icomatic s.p.a. Italy)
113 Leamore Lane, Walsall, West Midlands
Telephone 0922 75666   *Telex* Bircom G 338024

Capital Bearings Ltd.
Apex House, Stonefield Close, South Ruislip,
Middlesex HA4 0LD
Telephone 01-845 3511 or 01-845 0354
Telex 848314 Chamcon Slough

Charman Machinery Ltd.
Colonels Lane, Chertsey, Surrey KT16 8RH
Telephone Chertsey 65125

Concentric Production Research Ltd.
Reddicap Trading Estate, Sutton Coldfield,
West Midlands B75 7DE
Telephone 021-378 3030   *Telex* 336249 Alcon G

Anthony H. Croucher Ltd.
Holybourne, Nr. Alton, Hampshire GU34 4HK
Telephone Alton 82507, 82868 or 83242

Driver Southall Ltd.
Tame Bridge, PO Box 86, West Bromwich Road,
Walsall, West Midlands WS5 4BD
Telephone 0922 614631   *Telex* 338186

Derek W. S. Durance (Machine Tools)
28 Lime Kiln Road, Mannings Heath,
Horsham RH13 6JH
Telephone 0403 67050

Hahn & Kolb (GB) Ltd.
6 Forum Drive, Leicester Road, Rugby, Warwickshire
Telephone 0788 74261

INA Automation
(Division of INA Bearing Co. Ltd.)
Castle Vale Industrial Estate, Minworth,
Sutton Coldfield, West Midlands
Telephone 021-351 4047   *Telex* 338304

Sidney G. Jones Ltd.
(Agents for Sortmat Machines)
8 Balham Hill, London SW12 9EA
Telephone 01-673 5611   *Telex* 28723

Manifold Indexing Ltd.
Seymour Road, Leyton, London E10 7LZ
Telephone 01-556 1834   *Telex* 897034

Mattock Engineering Services Ltd.
74 Melton Road, Barrow-on-Soar,
Loughborough, Leicestershire
Telephone Quorn 42859

Mechanised Assembly Ltd.
Worcester Trading Estate, Blackpole Road,
Worcester WR3 8SQ
Telephone 0905 54141   *Telex* 339729

Modine Pneumatic Ltd.
Greengate Works, 2 New Bridge Street, Greengate,
Salford M3 7WP
Telephone 061 832 9671   *Telex* 668328

Multi Pneumatics Ltd.
Unit 9, Broadground Road, Lakeside Industrial
Estate, Redditch, Worcestershire B98 8YR
Telephone 0527 22660

CONTINUED

Henry Pels & Co. Ltd.
32-38 Osnaburgh Street, London NW1 3NE
Telephone 01-387 4113   *Telex* 25411

Placements Ltd.
21 Denham Gardens, Castlecroft Road,
Wolverhampton
Telephone 0902 763649

Podmores (Engineers) Ltd.
Winton House, Stoke Road, Stoke-on-Trent,
Staffordshire
Telephone 0782 45361

Powell Manufacturing Co. (Coventry) Ltd.
Cromwell Street, Coventry CV6 5EX
Telephone 0203 85131

Redman Engineering Ltd.
P.O. Box 16, Hawkesworth Industrial Estate,
Swindon, Wiltshire SN2 1EH
Telephone 0793 26394   *Telex* 449661

Rhoden Partners Ltd.
231 The Vale, London W3 7QU
Telephone 01-743 4562

Riley Equipment
NEI International Combustion Ltd., Sinfin Lane,
Derby DE2 9GJ
Telephone 0332 23223   *Telex* 37581 Energy G

Roevac Automation Ltd.
Grey Street, Denton, Manchester M34 3RT
Telephone 061 336 3857   *Telex* 51347

Russell Autofeeds Ltd.
Technical Division, Central Works, Studley,
Warwickshire B80 7AS
Telephone 052785 2301   *Telex* 51347

Sciaky Electric Welding Machines Ltd.
212 Bedford Avenue, Trading Estate, Slough,
Berkshire SL1 4RH
Telephone Slough 25551   *Telex* 847254

Snyder Automation Ltd.
Waddensbrook, Wednesfield,
Wolverhampton WV11 3SS
Telephone 0902 65363   *Telex* 338135

Spirol Industries Ltd.
Princewood Road, Corby,
Northamptonshire NN17 2ET
Telephone 05366 67634   *Telex* 342288

Swissap
29 Waterloo Place, Leamington Spa CV32 5LA
Telephone 0926 32222   *Telex* 312133

Taylor Hitec Ltd.
(Advanced Engineering Technology)
77 Lyons Lane, Chorley, Lancashire PR6 0PB
Telephone Chorley 5825
Telex 67202 (BR Taylor Chorly)

Unimatic Engineers Ltd.
122 Granville Road, Cricklewood, London NW2 2LN
Telephone 01-455 0012   *Telex* 922396

Valley Automation Ltd.
Valley Road, Lye, Stourbridge D79 8JH
Telephone Lye 2324 or 2419   *Telex* 388212 Valley

Vaughan Associates Ltd.
Abbeyfield Road, Nottingham NG7 2SU
Telephone 0602 862591   *Telex* 37527

VSI Automation Co. Ltd.
194 Stanley Green Road, Poole, Dorset BM15 3AW
Telephone 0202 624727   *Telex* 21792 or 2565

Wickman Machine Tool Sales (Assembly Division)
Herald Way, Brandon Road, Binley,
Coventry CV3 2NY
Telephone 0203 450810   *Telex* 311521

APPENDIX 3

BUYER'S GUIDE

MANUFACTURERS AND SUPPLIERS LISTED ACCORDING TO PRODUCTS

HOPPER FEEDERS
ALBE (ENGLAND) LTD.
AYLESBURY AUTOMATION LTD.
BRANDONE MACHINE TOOL LTD.
DRIVER SOUTHALL LTD.
INA AUTOMATION
SIDNEY G. JONES LTD.
MECHANISED ASSEMBLY LTD.
MULTI PNEUMATICS LTD.
PODMORES (ENGINEERS) LTD.
REDMAN ENGINEERING LTD.
RILEY EQUIPMENT
SWISSAP
VALLEY AUTOMATION LTD.
VSI AUTOMATION CO. LTD.
WICKMAN MACHINE TOOL SALES
(Assembly Division)

LINEAR FEEDERS
PODMORES (ENGINEERS) LTD.
VSI AUTOMATION CO. LTD.

LOADING AND ORIENTATING ELEVATORS
AYLESBURY AUTOMATION LTD.
INA AUTOMATION
VALLEY AUTOMATION LTD.
VSI AUTOMATION CO. LTD.

ROTARY TRANSFER EQUIPMENT
ALBE (ENGLAND) LTD.
AYLESBURY AUTOMATION LTD.
BADALEX LTD.
BRANDONE MACHINE TOOLS LTD.
BROWN AND WARD LTD.

ROTARY TRANSFER EQUIPMENT *continued*
CAPITAL BEARINGS LTD.
CHARMAN MACHINERY LTD.
CONCENTRIC PRODUCTION RESEARCH LTD.
SIDNEY G. JONES LTD.
MANIFOLD INDEXING LTD.
MATTOCK ENGINEERING SERVICES LTD.
MECHANISED ASSEMBLY LTD.
MODINE PNEUMATICS LTD.
HENRY PELS & CO. LTD.
PLACEMENTS LTD.
POWELL MANUFACTURING CO. LTD.
REDMAN ENGINEERING
SCIAKY ELECTRIC WELDING MACHINES LTD.
SNYDER AUTOMATION LTD.
SWISSAP
TAYLOR HITEC LTD.
UNIMATIC ENGINEERS LTD.
VSI AUTOMATION CO. LTD.
WICKMAN MACHINE TOOL SALES
(Assembly Division)

LINEAR TRANSFER EQUIPMENT
ALBE (ENGLAND) LTD.
AYLESBURY AUTOMATION LTD.
BADALEX LTD.
BROWN AND WARD LTD.
CAPITAL BEARINGS LTD.
CHARMAN MACHINERY LTD.
SIDNEY G. JONES LTD.
MANIFOLD INDEXING LTD.
MECHANISED ASSEMBLY LTD.
MULTI PNEUMATICS LTD.
HENRY PELS & CO. LTD.
PODMORES (ENGINEERS) LTD.
POWELL MANUFACTURING CO. LTD.

LINEAR TRANSFER EQUIPMENT *continued*

REDMAN ENGINEERING
RILEY EQUIPMENT
ROEVAC AUTOMATION LTD.
SCIAKY ELECTRIC WELDING MACHINES LTD.
SNYDER AUTOMATION LTD.
SWISSAP
TAYLOR HITEC LTD.
UNIMATIC ENGINEERS LTD.
VALLEY AUTOMATION LTD.
VSI AUTOMATION CO. LTD.
WICKMAN MACHINE TOOL SALES
    (Assembly Division)

ORIENTATING MECHANISMS

ALBE (ENGLAND) LTD.
AYLESBURY AUTOMATION LTD.
BRANDONE MACHINE TOOL LTD.
BROWN AND WARD LTD.
CHARMAN MACHINERY LTD.
CONCENTRIC PRODUCTION RESEARCH LTD.
INA AUTOMATION
MECHANISED ASSEMBLY LTD.
HENRY PELS & CO. LTD.
REDMAN ENGINEERING
RILEY EQUIPMENT
ROEVAC AUTOMATION LTD.
SNYDER AUTOMATION LTD.
VALLEY AUTOMATION LTD.
VSI AUTOMATION CO. LTD.
WICKMAN MACHINE TOOL SALES
    (Assembly Division)

ESCAPEMENT MECHANISMS

AYLESBURY AUTOMATION LTD.
BRANDONE MACHINE TOOL LTD.
BROWN AND WARD LTD.
CHARMAN MACHINERY LTD.
CONCENTRIC PRODUCTION RESEARCH LTD.
DEREK W. S. DURANCE (Machine Tools)
INA AUTOMATION
MECHANISED ASSEMBLY LTD.
PLACEMENTS LTD.
PODMORES (ENGINEERS) LTD.
REDMAN ENGINEERING
RILEY EQUIPMENT
ROEVAC AUTOMATION LTD.
SNYDER AUTOMATION LTD.
UNIMATIC ENGINEERS LTD.
VALLEY AUTOMATION LTD.
VSI AUTOMATION CO. LTD.
WICKMAN MACHINE TOOL SALES
    (Assembly Division)

COMPONENT PLACEMENT MECHANISMS

AYLESBURY AUTOMATION LTD.
BADALEX LTD.
BROWN AND WARD LTD.
CHARMAN MACHINERY LTD.
DEREK W. S. DURANCE (Machine Tools)
INA AUTOMATION
MECHANISED ASSEMBLY LTD.
MULTI PNEUMATICS LTD.
PLACEMENTS LTD.
REDMAN ENGINEERING
ROEVAC AUTOMATION LTD.
SNYDER AUTOMATION LTD.
SWISSAP
TAYLOR HITEC LTD.
VSI AUTOMATION CO. LTD.
WICKMAN MACHINE TOOL SALES
    (Assembly Division)

NUT RUNNERS

AYLESBURY AUTOMATION LTD.
BRANDONE MACHINE TOOL LTD.
BROWN AND WARD LTD.
CONCENTRIC PRODUCTION RESEARCH LTD.
SIDNEY G. JONES LTD.
MECHANISED ASSEMBLY LTD.
MULTI PNEUMATICS LTD.
REDMAN ENGINEERING
SWISSAP
VSI AUTOMATION CO. LTD.
WICKMAN MACHINE TOOL SALES
    (Assembly Division)

PIN INSERTERS

AYLESBURY AUTOMATION LTD.
BRANDONE MACHINE TOOL LTD.
BROWN AND WARD LTD.
CHARMAN MACHINERY LTD.
CONCENTRIC PRODUCTION RESEARCH LTD.
MECHANISED ASSEMBLY LTD.
MULTI PNEUMATICS LTD.
PLACEMENTS LTD.
REDMAN ENGINEERING
RUSSELL AUTOFEEDS LTD.
SPIROL INDUSTRIES LTD.
VSI AUTOMATION CO. LTD.
WICKMAN MACHINE TOOL SALES
    (Assembly Division)

RIVETING HEADS

AYLESBURY AUTOMATION LTD.
BRANDONE MACHINE TOOL LTD.
BROWN AND WARD LTD.
CONCENTRIC PRODUCTION RESEARCH LTD.
DEREK W. S. DURANCE (Machine Tools)
INA AUTOMATION

RIVETING HEADS *continued*
SIDNEY G. JONES LTD.
MECHANISED ASSEMBLY LTD.
HENRY PELS & CO. LTD.
REDMAN ENGINEERING
SWISSAP
WICKMAN MACHINE TOOL SALES
(Assembly Division)

AUTOMATIC SCREWDRIVERS
AYLESBURY AUTOMATION LTD.
BRANDONE MACHINE TOOL LTD.
BROWN AND WARD LTD.
CHARMAN MACHINERY LTD.
CONCENTRIC PRODUCTION RESEARCH LTD.
INA AUTOMATION
SIDNEY G. JONES LTD.
MECHANISED ASSEMBLY LTD.
HENRY PELS & CO. LTD.
PODMORES (ENGINEERS) LTD.
RUSSELL AUTOFEEDS LTD.
SPIROL INDUSTRIES LTD.
SWISSAP
VSI AUTOMATION CO. LTD.
WICKMAN MACHINE TOOL SALES
(Assembly Division)

SPRING FEEDING DEVICES
BADALEX LTD.
BROWN AND WARD LTD.
CONCENTRIC PRODUCTION RESEARCH LTD.
MECHANISED ASSEMBLY LTD.
RILEY EQUIPMENT
VSI AUTOMATION CO. LTD.

CONTROL SYSTEMS
BADALEX LTD.
CHARMAN MACHINERY LTD.
CONCENTRIC PRODUCTION RESEARCH LTD.
DEREK W. S. DURANCE (Machine Tools)
MECHANISED ASSEMBLY LTD.
MODINE PNEUMATICS LTD.
MULTI PNEUMATICS LTD.
RILEY EQUIPMENT
SCIAKY ELECTRIC WELDING MACHINES LTD.
TAYLOR HITEC LTD.
UNIMATIC ENGINEERS LTD.
VSI AUTOMATION CO. LTD.
WICKMAN MACHINE TOOL SALES
(Assembly Division)

STANDARD CHASSIS
AYLESBURY AUTOMATION LTD.
BADALEX LTD.
CHARMAN MACHINERY LTD.
INA AUTOMATION
MATTOCK ENGINEERING SERVICES LTD.
MECHANISED ASSEMBLY LTD.
MULTI PNEUMATICS LTD.
ROEVAC AUTOMATION LTD.
VAUGHAN ASSOCIATES LTD.
VSI AUTOMATION CO. LTD.
WICKMAN MACHINE TOOL SALES
(Assembly Division)

AUTOMATIC TESTING EQUIPMENT
BROWN AND WARD LTD.
WICKMAN MACHINE TOOL SALES
(Assembly Division)

DESIGN AND MANUFACTURE OF AUTOMATED ASSEMBLY MACHINES FOR SPECIFIC APPLICATIONS
AYLESBURY AUTOMATION LTD.
BROWN AND WARD LTD.
CHARMAN MACHINERY LTD.
CONCENTRIC PRODUCTION RESEARCH LTD.
ANTHONY H. CROUCHER LTD.
DEREK W. S. DURANCE (Machine Tools)
SIDNEY G. JONES LTD.
MECHANISED ASSEMBLY LTD.
PLACEMENTS LTD.
POWELL MANUFACTURING CO. LTD.
RHODEN PARTNERS LTD.
VAUGHAN ASSOCIATES LTD.
VSI AUTOMATION CO. LTD.
WICKMAN MACHINE TOOL SALES
(Assembly Division)

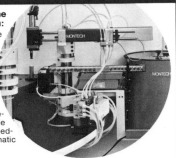
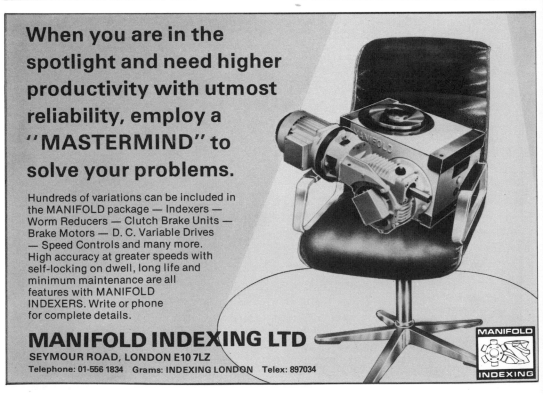

Aylesbury Automation can help you increase production now!

Parts feeding, parts movement, assembly, automatic counting . . . these are our specialities. To back them up we offer advanced products and systems plus in-depth advice — to help you cut costs, raise efficiency and increase productivity. Call our design team now. At your service to discuss your next project and design and manufacture the machines you need.

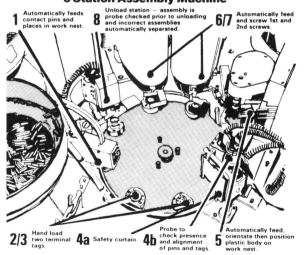

Aylesbury Automation's Automatic & Semi-Automatic Machines are increasing productivity now!

Modular, automatic or semi-automatic assembly machines like this can be tailor-made for *your* product, adapting the modular units which are also available separately. This semi-automatic, variable speed machine produces approximately 20 light socket units a minute and incorporates a safety cut out at the manual loading station. Just one example of Aylesbury Automation versatility.

8 Station Assembly Machine

1 Automatically feeds contact pins and places in work nest.

8 Unload station — assembly is probe checked prior to unloading and incorrect assemblies automatically separated.

6/7 Automatically feed and screw 1st and 2nd screws.

2/3 Hand load two terminal tags.

4a Safety curtain.

4b Probe to check presence and alignment of pins and tags.

5 Automatically feed, orientate then position plastic body on work nest.

Find out how we can help you today.

Aylesbury Automation Ltd
Suppliers of cost cutting equipment.

Assembly Machines - Vibration Parts Feeders - Centrifugal Feeders - Elevating Hopper Feeders & Loaders - Counting Systems - Feeding & Placement Systems - Special Purpose Machines.

PO Box 2, Mandeville Road, Aylesbury, Bucks HP21 8AB Tel: Aylesbury (0296) 5911 Telex: 83210

 *A member of the Bifurcated Engineering Group.*

Feeding & Transfer systems.

We offer a wide variety of vibratory bowl feeders, horizontal take-off feeders, gravity magazines and other auxillary handling equipment which may be necessary as part of a system. Acoustic shrouds for the vibratory bowl feeders are available to cover the range of sizes.

We are manufacturers of vibratory feeding and elevating equipment of every description, Vibratory feeders, and conveyors, spiral elevators, both powered by vibrator motors and also electro-magnetically operated.

We would be only too pleased to consider any feeding problems that you have. Alternatively send for illustrated literature.

Valley Automation Limited, Valley Road, Lye, Stourbridge DY9 8JH.
Tel: Lye 2324.
Telex: 338212 Valley.

Valley
Automatic Feeders.

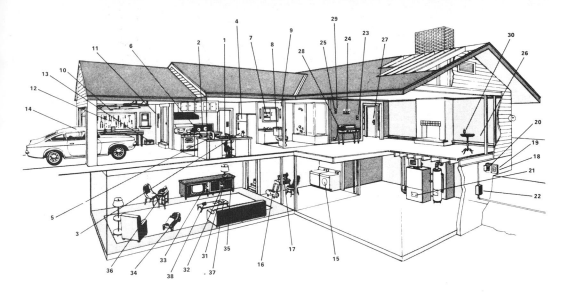

A Vaun Bodine machine can assemble just about anything around the house.
And save you up to 95% of your assembly costs.

Typical assemblies include:-

1 Taps
2 Kitchen Utensils
3 Detergent Pumps
4 Refrigerator Controls
5 Appliance Motors
6 Torches
7 Razors
8 Toilet Valves
9 Fluorescent Fittings

10 Garage Door Locks
11 Hedge Trimmers
12 Hand Tools
13 Padlocks
14 Over 50 Components for cars
15 Washing Machine controls
16 Vacuum Cleaner flex reel sets
17 Sewing Machine Components
18 Fuse Boxes
19 Circuit Breakers

20 Fuses
21 Boiler Controls
22 Water Meters
23 Light Switches
24 Light Fittings
25 Thermostats
26 Double Light Sockets
27 Door Knobs
28 Telephone Components
29 Air Conditioning Controls

30 Cigarette Lighters
31 Radio Components
32 Stereo Cartridges
33 Television Controls
34 Toys
35 Tape Cassettes
36 Typewriter Components
37 Pens
38 Cameras

The field of application is vast and if you produce an assembly in large quantities
it will pay you to discuss it with us.
Write or phone:—

 **SPECIALISTS IN THE DESIGN AND MANUFACTURE OF ASSEMBLY, INSPECTION AND PRODUCTION AUTOMATION.**

VAUGHAN ASSOCIATES LIMITED
Trent Works, Abbeyfield Rd., Nottingham NG7 2SU. Tel : 0602 862591 Telex : 31 537
Head Office : 4 Queen St., London W1X 8AN

P 1396

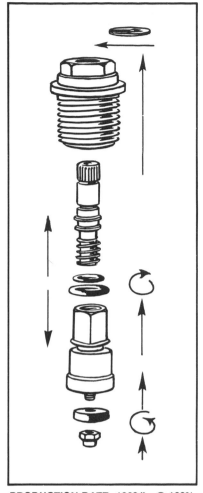
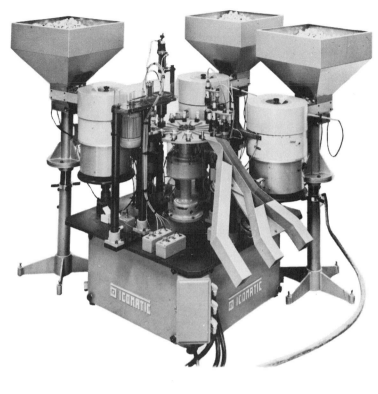

Other Production
DATA MEMORANDA

*Published by
The Institution of Production Engineers*

In Process Materials Handling
This publication follows the same format as the rest of the series but illustrates handling systems and provides the reader with standard information on some of the accepted methods of conveying materials that are available and in current use within industry.
Code No. 176.2.

Pre-Set Tooling
The need for pre-set tooling can be clearly seen in the savings that can be achieved in machine tool setting time, in the increase of machine tool utilisation and consequently in greater productivity.

With the introduction of numerically controlled machinery, the need for this saving becomes apparent. Due to the high rate of production from these machines, the cost of 'down time' can be excessive.

This Data Memoranda illustrates and describes the best pre-setting practices currently employed in British Industry and offers guidance on a suitable relationship that a setting section should have with other departments within a manufacturing concern.
Code No. 176.1.